Fourteen Fridays

A story of baseball, church, data & redemption

by

Eric Swanson and Matt Engel

FOURTEEN FRIDAYS
A story of baseball, church, data & redemption

This book is a fictional dramatization based on real events and was drawn from a variety of sources, including the 2019 season of the Colorado Rockies, published materials, web-based resources and our work with some of the best churches in the country. For dramatic and narrative purposes, this book contains fictionalized scenes, composite and representative characters and dialogue of people we know who have led the way in this data journey. The views and opinions expressed in the book are those of the book's characters only and do not necessarily reflect or represent the views and opinions held by individuals on which those characters are based.

Cover Design: Eric Swanson, Matt Engel and Roussdesign

Print ISBN: 978-1-63821-199-0
Ebook ISBN: 978-1-63821-200-3

Table of Contents

Acknowledgements

We wish to acknowledge and sincerely thank those who helped shape the path and form the story of *Fourteen Fridays*, beginning with our visionary colleagues at Leadership Network, Dave Travis, Greg Ligon, Julia Burk and Brent Dolfo, who wanted to help make data as common as running water for churches. We want to thank the seventy innovative, influential and impactful churches who jumped on board as early adopters and provided the data validations, that for the longest time were mere hunches. They helped turn our "what if" into "we know."

We want to thank those early readers, without whose feedback, would allow us to live in the delusion that we could get it right the first time. Specifically, we want to thank our spouses, Liz Swanson and Denise Engel, for being our very first readers. For those who took the time to read and give helpful feedback, we thank Brent Dolfo, Jeff Bojar, Brian Carson, Jake Chacko, Tom Nealley, Derek Maxson, Laura Seredinski, Dave Travis, Jeff Caliguire, Chris Chan, Andy Swanson, Rachel Finley, Ross Chapman, Edmund Lam, Kevin Kelley, Scott Beck, Kim Saquing, Michael Lukaszewski, Olivia Kruse, Lincoln McIlravy, Susie Richardson and Rabs.

A special shout-out to Renee Bennett, Linda Glaze, Dan Hauser and Lisa Mathews for their attention to detail and to Mike Lewis, who helped us craft a better ending.

We want to thank our distant story mentors; Lisa Cron, Shawn Coyne, Stephen King, Donald Miller and Robert McKee, who remind us, that in a good story, all is not as it seems.

Finally, we thank Roussdesign in Morocco, whom we hired through Fiverr, who got this book ready for publication on both the print and Kindle versions.

To all of you and un-named others who helped along the way, thank you.

Preface

Four years ago, we began a great experiment working with many of the leading churches in America in order to help them discover the answer to our big question: "How might we use data, analytics and messaging to do the five things every church must master to thrive and grow?" This book is a compilation of our collective hypotheses, experiments and learnings that have come out of that four-year journey.

We find ourselves fascinated with the idea that "fiction is the lie through which we tell the truth." With that in mind, although the characters are mostly fictional, every one of the experiments, data sets and examples are all true and create a genuine path forward for you and your church to grow and thrive as never before. Some names were changed to protect the innocent….and the guilty, but all of this actually happened…just as it is written.

Fourteen Fridays reflects the actual 2019 Colorado Rockies Schedule. We watched the summary of each game on YouTube and recreated the action by reading the detailed box score at baseball-reference.com. All of the data on win expectancy was found on gregstoll.com.

If you find yourself mired in the weeds of the data conversations between Tom and Bob, just skim those parts and resume with the story. All the valuable information you need to successfully run data experiments is found in the appendices.

Every story has a "before" and "after" that involves some type of transformation of the protagonist. It's our hope that by the end of this book you too will have a before and after story and be changed for the better.

So, here's to you—the dreamers, the fire-starters, the hungry, the frustrated, the disenchanted, the early adopters, the Executive Pastors, the dismissed, the businesspeople on church boards, the quants and data dogs who get it, but never get a seat at the table. Your day is coming. Stay hopeful. Take us boldly into the future with data. It's part of the language of God.

God bless you and welcome to the journey.

Eric and Matt

Chapter one

Tom looked up from what was left of his salad. Had she really said that? Did she really mean it?

"Wait...what did you say?" asked Tom.

"Maybe it's time you did something else Tom," said Amy. "You work so hard and are so under-appreciated. Maybe it's the Lord's way of telling you it's time to move on."

"I can't believe you're saying this, Amy. I'm not a quitter. You know that. And I didn't think you were either. I love the church and I think if we just started a third service, we'd..."

"Tom!" Amy interrupted. "You might love the church, but you don't love really love *this* church, do you? And by the way they treat you, I suspect they really don't love you...or me. I mean you're working so hard to make this church grow that we hardly see each other and when you're home you are on the phone or your computer resolving this or that. Maybe you can live like this, but I can't for much longer. I miss my Tommy."

Tom wanted to fight back but no surge of adrenaline came to his aid and he suspected that she was not far off the mark. "Amy, we agreed before we came here, that coming to Denver to turn this church around was the right thing to do. They could have asked a dozen other pastors, but the denomination asked me. You were so confident that I could do this. There was a time when we both felt called to church ministry."

Amy reached across the table and cupped Tom's free hand between her own. "Honey, I'm not going anywhere. Maybe I'm overreacting because I just miss the life we had together before coming here. You can't keep beating your head against the wall. But as long as your heart is in it, I'm here by your side."

Tom gave a faint smile and placed his right hand on top of Amy's.

"How about if I make some popcorn and we'll watch a movie like we used to," invited Amy.

"I so wish we could," Tom said longingly. "But I've got that elder meeting tonight. I better go. But...thanks...just thanks. It's going to work out. I promise you."

Tom found his way out of the apartment and took the stairwell to the underground parking where he hurried to his car. Denver's brisk March air reminded him that he should have grabbed his parka as it would really be cold when he returned. He got into his car and drove off towards the church that he had pastored for the past six months. Hopefully, this would be a good elder meeting.

At the elder meeting

Harold Haynie, the lead elder, called the meeting to order promptly at 7pm. Tom opened the meeting with prayer and a short devotional from *My Utmost for His Highest*. After the reading and approval of the minutes from the February's meeting, Harold reviewed the night's agenda. Until tonight, Tom had seen elder Harold as a good man...just wound a bit tight perhaps. Harold and his younger brother, Ron, grew up in Daybreak Church, then Tenth Street Baptist Church, under the Bible teaching of Pastor Arnie Shaw. Growing up with an alcoholic and abusive father, Pastor Arnie served as a worthy role model and father figure to Harold and Ron. Harold had graduated from Bob Jones University and, though the only thing he'd ever flirted with was the idea of going into ministry, he chose teaching Bible and math at Werx Christian Academy, a private school in Denver, which seemed to suit him very well. His brother, Ron, became a pastor of a large church in Ohio but was hinting that he wanted to get back to Colorado.

Elder Harold was in his early forties when he and June were married. Harold carried a torch for June since they were in the youth group at Tenth Street Baptist Church, twenty-five years earlier. Harold found it hard to believe his good fortune when he learned that June was back in Denver on furlough with Overseas Missionary Fellowship. So, after a week of prayer and fasting, Harold talked to June's father to ask permission to court June. They were married in the church three months later. Pastor Arnie performed the ceremony. Harold and his bride were very active at Daybreak Church, taught the class on biblical marriage and he and June seemed to have a solid, loving marriage though at times Harold seemed more of a parent than a partner. The few times that Tom and Amy had been on a double date with Harold and June, Harold would often override June's dinner order with a comment like, "Oh, you know that the fettuccini will give you heartburn. She'll take Caesar salad with dressing on the side." Harold once said that he and June never used the "D" word... "Divorce," as a hedge around their marriage. If they never talked about divorce, they could never get one. It wouldn't be too long before his certainty and his reality would bump into each other.

Whether intentional or not, Harold's spirituality often took center stage. Tom guessed it was genuine but wasn't sure he wanted a church full of those types of "mature" believers who were so certain about everything. Harold had memorized large portions of Scripture...way more than Tom had...so Tom never wanted to get into a scriptural squabble with Harold. Whereas Tom would often process his thoughts verbally while formulating his ideas, Harold was measured and had mastered the use of pauses and intimidating silence. More than once, Harold had quoted the proverb about a fool blurting out every foolish thing that came to mind, and the wisdom of silence. Tom felt lately that remarks like that almost always were directed at him. Harold was only a couple years older than Tom, but Harold comported himself like he was decades older and wiser than Tom but maybe Tom was overthinking it.

Harold was the first congregant to befriend Tom when he arrived as the new lead pastor at Daybreak Church last September. Harold and Tom met every Tuesday morning for breakfast at Denny's for the first four months and Tom felt he had found a real friend in

Harold. Once a month they had a couple's dinner together. Friendships and pastorates don't always go hand-in-hand, so Tom felt his budding friendship with Harold was a confirmation of God's calling to move to Denver. He had found a real friend and confidant. Tom had opened up about some of his personal failures, temptations, besetting sins and struggles in his marriage and they were received with grace and understanding. It felt good to get everything out in the open with a trusted and godly friend like Harold. Brené Brown had made it fashionable to be vulnerable and Tom felt vulnerable with Harold. But things were different now. For the past two months, Harold had been avoiding Tom. The Tuesday breakfasts and double dates had ceased altogether. Tom realized that Harold knew so much about himself, but Tom knew so little about Harold. He was about to find out more.

Harold reviewed the month-over-month numbers around attendance and giving with the precision of an accountant. Average weekend attendance was down by 214 from a year ago and year-to-date giving was down eighteen percent from a year ago and they were coming into the summer months. Harold solemnly looked at Tom. What came next was the gut punch. "Last week I called a special meeting of the elders to discuss your six-month performance review," said Harold. Although Tom was at every elder meeting, he had a non-voting position so Harold's actions, though in line with the church constitution, felt like a secret backroom meeting that would lead to a coup. "On the recommendation of the District Superintendent, we agreed to call you to this church as our pastor in the hopes that you could turn this church around after Pastor Arnie went to be with the Lord," continued Harold. "But after much prayer and seeking the Lord, on behalf of the elders, I'll be blunt and get to the point. It is clear that because of your pastoral limitations, random, topical preaching and to be frank, some borderline moral issues, coupled with declining attendance and giving, the elders unanimously concluded that you have six months to turn this around or you will be terminated. This decision is not up for debate or argument. You can accept these terms or resign tonight."

Tom's face reddened and he felt the muscles in his shoulders tense. The back of his neck began to throb. He had never been fired from a job in his entire life and he had been working since he was fifteen. Why would Harold do this to me? he thought. Harold had taken, what was shared in confidence, and used it publicly against him. But why? Tom looked around the room for an ally but none of the other eight elders would look Tom in the eye. Tom wanted so desperately to fight back but was determined not to give Harold that satisfaction of watching him crack. He would bend but he would not break. He would not justify his actions. But he would speak. "Um...uh... I'll take what you've said into consideration and let you know by tomorrow evening," he said haltingly.

"There is no bargaining," said Harold. "There's no room for compromising here, Tom. Give us your decision right now. Do you want to take our generous six-month offer or resign tonight?"

Tom's head throbbed. His heart raced. He had never quit anything in his life and was not about to start. He needed time and space to think but was painted into a corner. His face reddened. "Well...then...I'll accept your offer to do what I can these next six months to serve and grow this church. I've got a lot to think about, so I'll leave the rest of the meeting to you elders." With that, Tom put his laptop into his backpack and quickly stepped out of the conference room. He was numb. What just happened? he thought. To be so falsely accused felt so painful. The church had declined a bit since he arrived in Denver, but it was in a free-fall before Daybreak Church had called him to be their pastor. What do I do? How will I tell Amy?

Tom drives home

Getting into his Honda CR-V, he picked up his phone. "Siri, call Dad."

"Calling Dad," Siri responded cheerfully.

"Hey Son. So glad you called. Your mother and I were just talking about you. How's it going out in Denver this evening? Didn't you have an elder meeting tonight? How'd it go?"

"Not too well, Dad." Tom went on to explain what happened that evening. "I don't know Dad, I think it was my pride that kept me from quitting on the spot. I've done my best but it's just not the same here in Colorado. I'm just not sure what I can do in the next six months to turn things around. I've tried everything I know how to do. But if I resign now, what would I do? I'm forty-eight years old and about to be put out on the street. I don't want to be one of those ex-pastors who sells insurance."

After a long silence, Tom's father spoke. "Let me see what I can do. I've got a friend who was a big part of our company when we were really taking off. He introduced me to a whole new world I knew nothing about. He was a founder of a data and analytics company here in the Bay Area but lives in Denver now. He really helped us get unstuck and move forward and was the most unlikely consultant we've ever hired. Super good guy. Not sure where he is with the Lord right now but if Jethro, the Midianite priest, could be useful to Moses, maybe Bob can be useful to you. Let me see what I can do to make an introduction."

"I don't know Dad. I...."

"'Couldn't hurt...might help,' as people say. I'll figure out a good way for you two to get some time together. It'll all work out. By the way have you bought any Rockies tickets yet?"

"Not yet. I mean there are tickets available for every game and Amy and I are only a couple blocks from Coors field, so it's no big deal to get to a game," answered Tom.

"Well, let me see what I can do."

Tom parked in the garage below his apartment, slowly plodded up the stairs, unlocked the door and with slumped shoulders entered through the door and slung his backpack over a kitchen chair. Tom looked down at their Australian Labradoodle, Riley Lu, who had come to the door to greet him. "Hello girl," he said flatly.

"You're home early," said Amy. Turning towards Tom, she blurted out, "You look awful. What happened?"

"I pretty much got fired tonight. It was awful." Feeling the humiliation, Tom began to tear up. Amy stepped towards Tom and wrapping her arms around his waist and putting her head to his chest she said, "Oh Tom...that's so unfair. Those jerks. Who was it...Harold?"

Tom nodded. "I don't know if I still have it in me, Amy. I just don't know anymore. I just thought if I preached from the Word and loved people then we would grow as a church. I'm just not sure anymore. Everything I learned in seminary...everything I did in Houston, just is not working here."

"We'll be okay Honey...we'll get through this and be okay. And if we don't, we'll figure out something else to do," said Amy. "Maybe it's time for a change."

"You know as well as I do, that pastoring is the only thing I've ever cared about. I don't have any business skills. What am I going to do? Sell insurance? I don't even think that job exists anymore. I feel so lost." Tom was grateful for Amy. Sure, they had their ups and downs lately but, in this moment, he so desperately needed to feel her embrace.

"Let me get some wine and a couple of glasses and then I want you to tell me exactly what happened tonight," said Amy, getting up and reaching into the cupboard for a wine bottle.

Tom finished his second glass of wine when he got to the part about calling his dad.

"I wonder what your dad is going to do, and I wish I knew more about this Bob guy," said Amy.

"Well...I've got six months to figure it out or it looks like we'll be back in Houston. Maybe I can get my old job back."

"Someone else has that job now Tom and I do have my job here in town," said Amy. "One way or another we're going to survive this."

Over the next week, Tom tried to make sense of what had happened at the elder meeting. He felt so under-appreciated by the elder board...so misunderstood. He replayed the scene in his mind over and over, rethinking what he should have said. But by the beginning of April, Tom had made up his mind that he would do his best to turn the church around. He just didn't know how he was going to do it.

One day in early April, before going up to their second-story apartment, Tom stopped at the mailbox, and opened a small, padded envelope and inside found a stack of tickets to the Colorado Rockies' baseball games along with note that simply said, "As Yogi Berra said, 'It ain't over till it's over' and it ain't over yet.' Love, Dad. P.S. You can do this!" A smile came over Tom's face. That was just like Dad—always encouraging...always believing that Tom could do anything...and Tom tried his best to live up to those high expectations. But now at 48 did he really need his dad's help? From the emotional lift he felt, apparently, he did. Tom leafed through the tickets. Hmmm...fourteen tickets...all on Friday nights except for the home-opener this Friday afternoon.

Chapter two

Tom pressed the Espresso button on his coffee maker and waited for the whirr of the coffee beans grinding...the pause...as the steam built its pressure then forced its way through ground coffee into a four-ounce cup he purchased in Italy, with Amy, a couple summers ago. Tom loved his coffee...the stronger the better. And he liked a caffeine boost before his morning run.

After a thirty-minute jog around a nearby park with Riley Lu, Tom took a quick shower, dressed, turned the nob on his espresso machine to receive a full cup of Café Americano, sat down at his desk in the guest bedroom and cracked open his Bible to the first chapter of Nehemiah. He was starting a new series this week called "Rebuilding Hope" based on the book of Nehemiah and he wanted to go over his sermon one more time. Hope could be Tom's strategy for now. Just hope that the future can be better than the past. If the elders wanted expositional preaching, by God, that's what they'd get, chapter by chapter through the book of Nehemiah. To his surprise Tom enjoyed what he was learning. He identified with Nehemiah. As Nehemiah went to Jerusalem to rebuild the broken-down wall, Tom had come to Denver to rebuild a broken-down church. Tom was haunted by the two questions Nehemiah asked in the opening verses of chapter 1— "Tell me about the city" and "Tell me about the people." Asking those two questions changed everything. What about *his* people? What about *his* city?

Amy walked into the kitchen toweling off her hair. "I love my Peloton. This morning I was riding through the Pyrenees in Spain. Hey, I'm going up to see Lucy this morning. We're having breakfast at Chautauqua Park and then hiking up to the Royal Arch."

Tom was disappointed that Amy would not be in church this morning but there still would be close to a thousand people who would be there, so he shrugged it off. "Say hi to your sister for me."

At church
In the 9am service Tom made his way onto the platform and began singing the final stanza of a well-known hymn.

Though millions have come, there's still room for one
Yes, there's room at the cross for you.

Pianist Millie Hondorf was in fine form that morning bringing the hymn to a close with a soul-touching crescendo.

"Yes, there is room at the cross for you, friend," said Tom. "Please turn in your Bibles to Nehemiah, chapter one."

After giving a bit of background about the context of Nehemiah Tom pointed out that the word "quest" and "question" come from the same root word and the right question sets us on a journey of discovery. "The questions we ask are more determinative of who we become than the answers we think we know." Tom felt it was a solid beginning to the book of Nehemiah. As he looked over the audience in the first service, there was Harold, looking down and slowly shaking his head. Tom felt deflated but soldiered on through the 11am service.

At home
It was Sunday afternoon and Tom had intended to watch the NCAA Regional Finals between Duke and Michigan State but had drifted off to slumberland midway through the second half. His nap was interrupted when Amy came through the door. "I'm home," she announced.

"Oh, hi Babe," said Tom, slowly sitting up. "How was your time with Lucy?"

"Breakfast was great and then Brent joined us, and we had a delightful hike up to the Royal Arch. I love being around those two. Brent is so thoughtful and kind to Lucy. Sometimes I think non-Christians have better marriages than Christians," Amy said.

Tom felt uncomfortable and a bit defensive. That's all he needed to hear. "What makes you say that, Amy?"

"I think Christians sometimes rely too much on God to give them a good marriage rather than working to have a great marriage. I think loneliness feels exactly the same for a Spirit-filled Christian as it does for a non-Christian. Time alone with God might bring you closer to God but not closer to your wife." Amy was on a roll. "All the Christians I know who are divorced would tell me, 'We'd never get divorced. We're Christians,' as if being a Christian is a substitute for doing the real work it takes to sustain a love relationship. A wedding ring with a cross on it is not a talisman for a good marriage." Tom looked down at his left hand.

"So, what are you saying Amy, that Christ makes no difference in our marriage?" asked Tom defensively.

"I hope he does, Tom. I suspect he wants to, but he'll work within his laws of sowing and reaping. Here's what Brent said today. Something like 'I really love Lucy but know as a human free agent, she could leave me tomorrow. So, I find myself thinking, what can I do today...what kind things can I do...how can I love her in such a way that leaving me would be the last thing she'd ever want to do.' I think as Christian we just 'trust God' to give us a good marriage and don't do the work required to have a great relationship."

Tom was frustrated but not sure what to say. Amy filled the silence. "Tom, we have a good marriage and I'm not going any place. It's been a tough adjustment, coming to Colorado, and you're under a lot of pressure now. I'm just saying we could be way more than we are but we're a little stuck now. So, what do you want to do for dinner?"

Tom felt a bit numb but didn't have the energy or will power to take Amy on. He had too much on his plate. "I'm good with a salad. I'm not very hungry."

At church in the all-hands staff meeting

Each Monday morning Tom held a two-hour all-hands staff meeting. When Tom took the job, six months earlier, the first thing he had to do, at the request of the elder board, was to reduce the staff from twenty-two to fifteen to be more proportional to their actual attendance, which had dropped from 1,500 to a thousand after the founding pastor, Arnie Shaw had died. Tom preferred being liked, so helping seven staff "find their next place of usefulness" was a tough way to start a new job. Trust with the staff was in short supply but Tom felt the worst was over and he was beginning to like the remaining staff, including the two he had hired—Jerome as Director of Spiritual Formation and Tanika as Director of Student Ministries.

Tom gave a short devotional at the beginning of each all-hands meeting and the simplest method he had found was to read the appropriate page out of Oswald Chambers' *My Utmost for His Highest*. Today's devotional was titled *Heedfulness v. Hypocrisy in Ourselves.* It fell flat with the staff but at least they heard the Word today, he thought.

As Tom was getting his bearing in his new surroundings, he was eager to hear from the staff about their sense of what was happening at Daybreak Church. "So yesterday I introduced two questions that Nehemiah asked that helped him know what to do: 'Tell me about the people' and 'tell me about the city.' So, as a relative newcomer to Denver and Daybreak Church, what can you tell me about the city and the people of Daybreak?" asked Tom.

All the answers were somewhat benign until Jerome raised his hand. "Here's what I've observed from the three months I've been here. Every area in which Denver is measuring progress; this church seems to be against." Now that statement got the staff off of their phones and looking at Jerome. He continued, "The people of Denver celebrate Pride Day and greater inclusion of LGBTQ people. They celebrate greater opportunities for women and immigrants. They take stands on social justice, Black Lives Matter and work actively on climate change issues. They take science seriously and those are the very things our church seems to be against. This church would never survive where I come from. We just seem to be out of step and against the progress everyone else wants to make. The trajectory of society has always moved towards greater inclusion of who could experience the American dream and yet in church, we seem to be about who we should be against. Let me read from Martin Luther King." Jerome looked down at his phone.

"The Church has been an echo rather than a voice, a taillight behind the Supreme Court and other secular agencies, rather than a headlight guiding men progressively and decisively to higher levels of understanding."

Fourteen Fridays - 14

We need to be the headlights in our city, and we need to make some changes if we're going to have an impact on this city."

Tom appreciated Jerome's boldness and candor. "Thanks Jerome. God calls us to be a faithful presence and sometimes God's ways are not man's ways."

"Well, maybe man's ways should become more like God's ways," Jerome rebutted confidently.

"Yeah, maybe they should," said Tom pensively.

Friday, April 5. Colorado Rockies v. Los Angeles Dodgers

It was Friday afternoon and the home opener for the Colorado Rockies and Tom was glad he had the aisle seat in row one, of Section 239. Tom knew to be on the second level, along the third base line was the best seat in the house. It was a sunny April afternoon and Coors Field was sold out for the home opener. This is going to be a good season and tickets to the fourteen Friday games were a great "Welcome to Denver" gift from his dad.

Bob Andrews, fit and in his early 40s, let his left-hand bounce lightly down the green railing to the first row of Section 239. Tom stood up to create space for Bob to pass into the row to find his seat next to his own. "Hey, I'm Bob—your dad's friend from the Bay Area. Did he tell you I'd be joining you?"

Tom extended his hand and returned the introduction. "I'm Tom and of course he told me," fudged Tom. Tom smiled, thinking, that's just like Dad. He's got us sitting next to each other at the Rockies games. I guess this explains why Dad sent me just one ticket. "Couldn't hurt...might help," he had said.

Tom and Bob had missed most of the pre-game ceremonies but did stand for the National Anthem and sang along with the Air Force Academy Band as cadets unfurled the 150' x 300' American Flag before the fireworks exploded and the fighter squadron executed their precision flyover.

Bob started the conversation around what he knew they would agree on. "Can you believe the weather we have for the home opener? Sunny and close to 60."

"And not a bad game to open with," Tom replied. "Shoot, this has to be a big year for the Dodgers, coming off of two back-to-back World Series appearances...of course they lost both times. But they're 5-2 so far this season so should be a good contender again this year. So much talent on this team."

"Yep," Bob nodded in agreement. So, if you don't mind my asking, "Why the Astro's ball cap?"

"My wife and I moved from Houston last November. I love the Astros and I loved seeing them whip the Dodgers in the Series in 2017. Man, that was sweet! I'll always be an Astros fan till the day I die."

"I was pretty impressed myself with that team," replied Bob. "Cellar-dwellers in 2014 and just three years later they were the world champs—just as Sports Illustrated predicted they would be back in 2014. They combined player development with a great understanding of player data and analytics. I like that combination."

"Yeah...all that Moneyball stuff," said Tom dismissively.

The third inning ended in a 1-1 tie and Bob started a new conversation picking up on Tom's recent move to Denver. "So, what caused you to leave the Lone Star state?"

"It's a bit complex but it seemed to be that combination of a job that needed doing matched with my experience, passion and abilities." Tom answered.

"Well, now you've got to tell me more since you put it that way," insisted Bob.

"I'm the new pastor of a church not far from where we are sitting. Back in Houston, in 2001, my wife and I started a church and over the next twelve years we grew it to a church of over two thousand weekend attenders. That sort of got the attention of my denomination so they asked me to take a regional job helping church planters start new churches in the Southeast part of the U.S. At that time there was a need and coupled with my relative success, it seemed to be a great fit. I absolutely loved helping those fresh-faced and hopeful young men and women...some of the best and most satisfying years of my life. All my efforts and expertise were multiplied through other leaders. That's a sweet spot to be in."

"So, why'd you leave the job you loved to come be a pastor in a strange town?" asked Bob.

Tom wistfully smiled, "I've been asking myself that question the last couple months. But the gist of it is that in our denomination we have more churches closing every year than we are starting and so I was asked if I would take on this challenge in how to turn around and grow a declining church. Being from Houston I felt like George Foreman who made his boxing comeback at age forty. He said something like, 'Every athlete asks himself two questions in life: 'Can I do it?' And 'Can I do it again?' I guess I wanted to find out if I could do it again...could I succeed in growing another church? I missed the direct contact with a consistent group of people who are trying to figure out life. Like I said, I do like a challenge and our kids are all out of school now and out on their own—taken jobs in different parts of the country so we really aren't tethered to Houston. My wife Amy grew up in Boulder and was anxious to get back to the mountains so moving to Denver was a logical move. We're in Douglas Apartments, a couple blocks north of here at Park and Walnut Street. We love living downtown and the church is just a short drive from here. Hope that wasn't too much info for you."

Bob thought for a moment and then replied, "Well my dad is also a pastor, so I get what you're saying. He's got a decent sized church out in Silicon Valley. I used to be really involved in church and even was on his staff for a while, but I'm not involved with church much anymore. But I think I understand where you're coming from. Church ministry is really hard work. There were a lot of days my dad would question, out loud, why God called him to ministry. He has a real engineer's brain—super logical and evidence-based so early on he had some real battles with the elders. But fortunately for him he also had a bunch of really sharp engineers and tech people from H.P., Oracle, and more recently from Facebook and Google as part of his congregation who he could bounce ideas off of. Dad's in his early 60s now but is one of those life-long learners. The tagline of their church is something like, 'Christ-centered, mission-driven, data-informed.' So, how's it been going for you so far?"

"I'd love to say it was going great, but it really hasn't been going all that well. To be honest…it really sucks. All the things I did back in Houston and with church planters in the South just seems to fall flat here in Denver. I feel like I was trained to minister in a world that no longer exists and I don't have what it takes to figure it out. But I'm not sure I could do anything else. It's not like I don't have faith and am not working hard. I'm just not seeing the results I'd hoped for and expected. And I've been given a six-month time-frame to turn things around or the elders tell me I'll be gone."

Bob nodded his head in sympathy…or was it pity?

For a moment Tom had the feeling he had violated the number one rule of a new friendship—sharing too much…too soon. But Bob was an empathetic listener and after a brief pause suggested, "I think it's time for a beer."

"I think I'll join you and maybe grab a hotdog. I haven't eaten since breakfast," said Tom.

By the 7th inning stretch the Dodgers had pulled ahead by the score of 9-1. And the Rockies' fans hadn't moved. It was the home-opener after all. The complimentary rally towels would have to remain in their laps for now. "So, what are the odds the Rockies will make a comeback, Bob?" asked Tom.

"I can check right now on this baseball app." Bob pulled his phone from his pocket and deftly moved his thumbs across the face of his iPhone. "Okay…let's see now…Okay," he repeated. "Since 1957 there have been 1,511 Major League games where the visiting team was leading by eight runs going into the bottom of the 7th inning. And the home team has made a comeback only four times. So, I think it's safe to say this game is over."

"Seriously?" asked Tom.
Bob nodded and put his phone back in his pocket. "And that's probably a simple illustration of predictive analytics—looking at what happened in the past to predict what might happen in the future."

Tom felt he had done all the talking so turned the conversation towards Bob. "What do you do to pay the bills Bob?" Tom asked. "I think my dad said you're some type of consultant?"

"That's right. I have a small consulting company now, but my background is in tech. I worked for 18-years with a company, I helped start, called Datanadec, out in Silicon Valley. It's a data and analytics company that provided back-end support to startups, mostly but we've done some work with existing companies, like your dad's company, some nonprofits and even a few megachurches. But when the company moved their operations to Nevada in 2016, Dana and I thought it was time to make a move, so I took a year off, travelled a bit and then settled here in Denver and we started a consulting business, helping leaders use data to make better business decisions. We've got three full-time consultants now. We live a bit south of here in the Glass House on Basset, if you know the area," Bob replied as he watched the ground crew drag the infield. "Have you ever thought about how understanding data could help you in what you're trying to do Tom?"

Tom tried to be as tactful as possible, so paused before answering. "I'm a ministry guy, Bob. If I'm doing my job right, I'm seeking the Lord, praying and seeking his mind on what we should be doing. I think data is good for business and even baseball, but I think if I looked to any source other than God and his Word, I'd be compromising who I am and what God has called me to do. And besides, the elders would never hear such a thing. As they like to quote, 'God has given us everything pertaining to life and godliness' through his Word. Why would they ever look to data as a solution?"

Bob took a sip of his beer and turned towards Tom. "Well, that's one way of looking at it. If you don't mind, I'd like to push back a bit. My dad thought differently about data. He always reminded his congregants that in the opening couple of chapters of both the Old and New Testament God counted things and assessed the quality of what he observed. That's what we call quantitative and qualitative data. What are 'good,' 'very good,' and 'not good' except points of qualitative data? What is 3,000 in Acts 2, if not quantitative data. See what my T-shirt says? It's a quote often attributed to Einstein:

INSANITY IS DOING THE SAME THING OVER AND OVER AGAIN AND EXPECTING DIFFERENT RESULTS

"At Datanadec somebody was always printing a T-shirt to accompany one of our business initiatives, so I have a couple dozen of these T-shirts. Growing up in the church and seeing the stubbornness of some pastors and even more of their boards, sometimes I think we need a faith-based version of Einstein's quote...something like this:

'For church people, insanity is doing the same thing over and over again (only this time with prayer) and expecting different results.'"

Fourteen Fridays - 18

Tom smiled a bit at Bob's unexpected and slightly irreverent comeback. But what he said about Christian insanity sort of rang true.

Over the next two innings the Rockies chipped away at the Dodgers lead. They were down 10-4 as they entered the bottom of the ninth. Rockies right-fielder, Charlie Blackmon led off by grounding out to the pitcher. Outfielder David Dahl provided a glimmer of hope for Rockies fans by whacking one over the right-field fence and Nolan Arenado was up next so few of the devoted were heading for the exits. The score was now 10-5.

"You gonna be here for the Phillies in a couple of weeks?" Tom asked as Arenado took the first called strike.

"Wouldn't miss it," said Bob, not taking his eyes off the batter. "Your dad sent me tickets to all the Friday night games. So, it looks like we'll be joined at the hip for a while. I like the Rockies, and this should be a good season."

Arenado let three balls go past him and found himself ahead of the count at 3-1 before popping out to second. The crowd breathed out a collective moan as their hopes leaked away. Two outs.

Former LSU star Trevor Story stepped up to the plate and took the first pitch for a ball. Story fouled off the second pitch. The third pitch came in at 96mph, a four-seam fastball right down the center of the strike zone. Story knew it was gone once he connected. He trotted round the bases. The Rockies were slowly chipping away at the Dodger's dominant lead.

Second baseman, Ryan McMahon, ended all hope for the Rockies, standing still as the third strike whizzed past him. The Rockies home opener would be recorded in the L column. But in baseball there's almost always a tomorrow.

"I'll see you in a couple weeks then," said Bob. "But I've got something for you that we can talk about next time." With that Bob pulled a 3x5 card out of his back pocket and began writing. Handing the card to Tom, they bid their goodbyes and Bob headed for the exit. Tom slipped the card into his shirt pocket and climbed the stairs and followed the jostling crowd, down the escalator, through the exit and on to 20th Street. Tom was glad he lived nearby and enjoyed the short walk home.

At home
Amy smiled as Tom closed the door behind him. "How was the game Honey?"

"Rockies lost but I had a good time. Sat next to a real nice guy. Bob! He's the one my dad wanted to introduce me to. Bob's dad is a pastor, so we talked a bit about church and a bit about his work with data. Apparently, Dad bought tickets for both of us for the next thirteen Friday night games. Expensive…but cheaper than therapy. I think Dad wants him to coach me…or mentor me. I'll have to see about that, but I did enjoy his company. He'll be at the game on the 19th, so we'll continue our conversation I imagine." Tom then remembered about the card Bob had given him. Pulling the card out of his shirt pocket, Tom read these words:

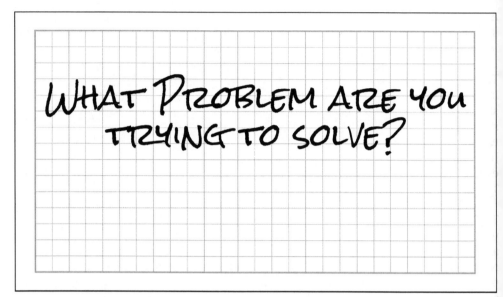

"That's so odd! 'What problem am I trying to solve?' I guess that's what he wants to talk about. Kind of nervy if you ask me. I hardly know the guy. You don't think he wants to talk about our marriage or anything personal do you Amy? I mean you and I don't have any real problems with our relationship, do we?"

Amy resisted rolling her eyes. The truth would have to wait for another day, so she avoided directly answering his question. "I think it's more about you and your job at church."

Tom went to the fridge. It was about supper time. "How 'bout if I throw a little salmon on the grill?

"Sounds yummy."

So, what problem am I trying to solve? Tom asked himself. I'll think about it in the morning.

Chapter three

At church

The Sunday services went well. It was "Compassion Sunday," a day for churches across America to share the Bible's message of caring for those in need and to give people the opportunity to sponsor a child through Compassion International. Thousands of churches were involved, and Tom was delighted that Daybreak was engaged in such a significant ministry. Compassion International was changing the world. After a short video highlighting the data on the positive outcomes for children who were sponsored, elder Harold took the stage where he explained the joy that he and June experienced through sponsoring a Compassion child. "The thrill of a lifetime was when June and I visited Maria and her family last summer in Guatemala. If heaven and earth ever came together for June and me, it was in Quetzaltenango with Maria and her family," Thirty new families signed up to sponsor children.

Tom finished his sermon out of Nehemiah 2 that morning asking the congregants what was broken in their world for which they needed help in rebuilding. They couldn't do it alone. He reminded them that help could come from godly people or pagans like Nebuchadnezzar... if they were open to it. After the first service as Tom stepped down off the platform, he tried to catch elder Harold's eye, but Harold was busy scribbling something on his bulletin. As Tom passed Harold, Harold handed Tom a note written neatly on the back of the attendance card.

*"**God's** work, done **God's** way, never lacks **God's** supply." Hudson Taylor*

"Learn from him! We don't need pagans to do God's work," admonished Harold.

At home

Tom was anxious to get home quickly after church. It was the final day of the Master's Golf Tournament in Augusta. Tom wasn't a huge golf fan but always had the final day of the Masters on his calendar. Tiger Woods came into Sunday two strokes behind Italy's Francesco Molinari. Tiger hadn't won a major tournament since 2008. In the interim he had four back surgeries and four knee surgeries. He was a welcome icon but not a potential champion. But Tiger was determined and at the end of the day, through skill and determination he was wearing the green jacket. If against all odds Tiger can do it, Tom thought, there's a chance I can make a comeback.

At church in the all-hands staff meeting

On Monday morning, Tom started the all-hands meeting with a devotional reading from Oswald Chambers daily devotional. Today's topic was on *"The Failure to Pay Close Attention"* and the fifteen staff were the perfect candidates for the talk because it seemed they were paying little attention to what Oswald had to say. A pastor always had to stay at least as interesting as what was on the screen in front of his audience and clearly Tom had failed that test. But what else could Tom do? There's got to be a better way to engage the staff.

Friday, April 19. Colorado Rockies v. Philadelphia Phillies

It was a 6:41 start against the Phillies, and because the temperature was in the mid 40s, Tom grabbed his parka, a wool hat and some mittens before starting his short walk to Coors Field. Baseball's starting times have been an anomaly since the days of radio, always starting five, seven, ten, or even eleven minutes past the hour or half-hour. This gives time for the broadcasters to announce the line-up, the national anthem and a quick commercial. The starting time reflects when the first pitch will be thrown. The game begins with the first pitch. By contrast, football games begin on the hour or half hour and, as part of the game, include the introductions, anthems and pageantry that precede the first kickoff.

Tom set out early, not just to beat the crowds but to grab a steak and potato burrito outside the entrance to Coors Field. As Tom descended the stairs, he found Bob already seated.

"Hey Tom," Bob said as he turned towards Tom. "How was your day?"

"Good," said Tom as he folded down his forest-green seat before settling in. After exchanging the usual niceties Tom started on a more serious topic. "Hey, I read that card you gave me a couple weeks ago...you know the one about what problems I'm solving? I'm not sure what you wanted me to do...I mean I have a lot of problems I'm trying to solve."

"Yeah, I probably should have been more specific. And I like that you said you have a lot of problems you're trying to solve," said Bob.

"Thanks a lot!" moaned Tom.

Determined to be understood Bob countered, "No, what I mean is that you only have problems if there is a goal you're trying to achieve or a mission you're trying to fulfill. No goals...no problems. Simple as that. So, when you said you have a lot of problems, I know you have a lot of dreams, desires...objectives that you want to see fulfilled. Problems are simply the obstacles we encounter on the way to fulfilling our mission. And that is a really good thing. To have problems is part of being fully alive."

"I hadn't thought of it that way," said Tom.

"But it is super-important to identify as specifically as we can, what we are really solving for. Look at my T-shirt, said Bob, unzipping his purple hoodie... "It's another one by Einstein.

"IF I HAD ONE HOUR TO SAVE THE WORLD, I'D SPEND THE FIRST 55 MINUTES DEFINING THE PROBLEM AND THEN FIVE MINUTES SOLVING IT."
ALBERT EINSTEIN

"I don't know that quote...but really 55 minutes defining the problem?"

"I don't want to be overly presumptuous since I'm not a pastor," said Bob, "but my dad is a pretty good pastor and this is something we talk about all the time, especially when he thinks I might have something to add from my data world. Dad figured out that every church, large or small, has the same five problems they are trying to solve, and I suspect these are the problems that keep you up at night. Every church planter has to solve for these same five things if his or her church is to grow and thrive. Every church that closes its doors for the last time has failed to solve for one or more of these five problems. These five problems had to be solved by the church at Pentecost and for every church in every culture since then—including online churches. Every children's pastor, youth minister, senior adult pastor or digital pastor has to solve these same five problems. These five motions are what my dad called his 'Church Engagement Framework' and though most churches are unaware of it, it still serves as every church's 'operating system'...whether a church is aware of it or not. Dad had so much engineer in him he always had analogies between engineering and his church."

Tom was more than curious, so wanted to know more. Could all he was trying to solve for really be found in just five words? "What do you mean by 'operating system?'"

"Good question." Bob thought for a moment. "Operating systems are simply the infrastructure or the backbone of every computer or smartphone that all the applications...you know...'apps' can run on. So, if you use Microsoft products, your operating system will be Microsoft Windows. Or if you're an Apple guy your operating system will be Apple OS or on your iPhone you have iOS. If you don't have an operating system none of the programs or apps will work. So, like computers or smartphones, although no two churches have the same programs, they all run off of this same five-part operating system...the Church Engagement Framework—whether they know it or not."

By now Tom's curiosity was vexingly piqued but now he and Bob were standing for the National Anthem. After sitting back down, Tom turned to Bob and asked, "Well aren't you going to tell me what those five things are that I'm supposed to be solving for?"

"Sure...thought you'd never ask," Bob smiled. "Well, the first thing every church has to do is *attract* people. Here's what I mean... 'Attract' simply means making people aware you exist and what comes to mind when people think of your church. What are you known for? 'Attract' doesn't necessarily mean that everyone in Denver knows you exist but of those you're trying to reach," Bob paused. "Say, millennials who live and work within a 5-mile radius of your church...how many of *them* know you exist? So 'Attract' is the first step you need to solve for in the Church Engagement Framework." Bob took a breath. "Make sense?"

Tom nodded.

"And the other part of 'Attract' is this—when people think of your church, what comes to their mind? What is it about your church that typically attracts people? Your preaching? Your Vacation Bible School? Your hospitality? Your facility? Are you known for what you're against or what you are for in the city? Are you about the thriving of those outside the church or are you seen as a club...just taking care of your own? So, 'Attract' is the first problem you have to solve for."

The Phillies got on the scoreboard quickly in the first inning and held a 1-0 lead going into the second inning. The thought of a church engagement framework was intriguing to Tom and he was both curious and eager to learn more about his church's operating system. "So, what are the other four parts of the framework Bob?" asked Tom as the Phillies started their batting order.

"Well, the second motion is to *get* folks into a church service or event for the first time...or maybe to watch your online service for the first time. We typically call these folks 'visitors' and they are a subset of all who have heard of your church. Do you have any idea why people visit Daybreak Church, Tom?" asked Bob.

"I'm not sure but I suppose someone in the church invited them," ventured Tom.

"That's probably true," continued Bob. "I remember reading that between 85 and 90 percent of folks who visited a church did so because they were simply invited. Every growing church simply has more people coming in the front door than people who are leaving through the back door. Every dying church has more people leaving the back door than are entering the front door."

"So, getting people through the front door is critical to the future of our church," said Tom.

"It may be *the* critical thing. And here's the good news. My dad sent me a link where the research shows that about 70 percent of people say they would visit a church if invited by a friend or family member," said Bob. "I don't know if that's true or not but it's something that could be tested."

The beer guy was at the top of the stairs and when Tom spotted him, he turned back to Bob. "I'm getting a Coors Light...you want something?"

"I'll take the same. Here's a ten," said Bob. "Tell him to keep the change."

"No, I got it," said Tom. And soon Tom and Bob were holding icy-cold brews.

"OK," said Tom after sipping the foam off the rim of his plastic cup, "so you've told me about attracting people and getting people. Let me guess what the third motion of the framework is. I'd say every pastor has to figure out how to *keep* the people who visit the church and how to close the back door."

"Yep, that's it," smiled Bob. "Pretty intuitive huh? Here's something my dad learned at an associational meeting...60 percent of people who visit a church three times make that church their home church."

"What...wait! What did you say?" asked Tom.

"I said," Bob slowed down, "that 60 percent of people who visit a church three times make that church their home church. So, the critical time for follow-up could be after the second visit if people actually identified themselves as visitors...which drives my dad crazy...the anonymity thing. My dad identified these second-time visits as 'data signals.'"

"What do you mean...'data signals?'" Tom leaned in.

"Well, my dad figured if someone visits his church one time, that person might be there because a friend invited them. But if a person lets it be known that they were there for a second time, that second visit served as a "data signal," signaling to my dad that either this person wanted to get closer to God, had some questions about life, or wanted to get involved in a community that was changing the world. In any case he made sure to personally give them a call after their second visit. That seemed to make a difference. Oh yeah, there was one other thing. When Dad started his church, he had this hypothesis that if visitors had dinner with him and mom that they'd more likely become part of the church. So, once a month they hosted a dinner at their house...and as the church grew, later at the church, for folks who had visited that month. It was just a hypothesis but what he discovered since then is that 83 percent of people who came to dinner joined the new members class and that percentage hasn't changed in 30 years. So, he turned a hypothesis into a fact—a 'what if...' into a 'what is.'"

"Woah...that's good," said Tom. That's something Amy and I could easily do."

The Phillies extended their lead, 2-0 going into the bottom of the fifth inning. Phillies pitcher, Vince Velazquez was throwing heat in the high 90s and had held the Rockies to just four hits. "So, I get 'attract,' 'get' and 'keep' but for the life of me I don't know what comes next," said Tom.

Bob drained the last of his beer, set the plastic cup back in the holder and said, "You'll recognize this one really fast because it's so tied to all you do."

Now Tom, a bit embarrassed by the fact he could not readily identify the fourth motion of the framework, said, "I'm sure I will but to save time...maybe you should just tell me?"

"Well, once people decide to stick around, what do you do with them? What are you doing with them now?" Bob asked. Bob had learned that when people discover something for themselves it sticks with them a whole lot longer.

"Well...I want them to grow in their relationship with Christ," began Tom.

Fourteen Fridays - 25

Bob smiled.

"Oh...Duh! *Grow* is the fourth motion!" said Tom.

Bob smiled even broader. "You got it! So, what do you do to grow your people Tom?"

"Well, we do a lot of things," replied Tom hesitantly. "My preaching, our First Steps class, we have small groups...a couple Sunday School classes...." And the more he talked the more uncertain he grew.

"Every church has a 'growth model' or 'change model' whether they recognize it or not. It's about inputs and outcomes," said Bob. "Here's how it goes: 'At our church we believe that if people do this...or do this and that...or do this, that and the other thing (which are your inputs) they become more of a disciple (which is the outcome.)' This is your de facto change model and here is the brilliance of having a change model...if you're not getting the outcomes you want, you can adjust the inputs and see if things improve."

"We have a ton of good programs at church...I mean they are all good. How do we know what works?" Then Tom lowered his voice and leaned in closer to Bob. "I see people who attend church every week and have been in the same Sunday School class for 20 years, but they are still mean-spirited, gossipy, bigoted and even racist. And some of these folks are on our elder board." Tom's stomach churned as he thought of that overly pious elder Harold.

Bob chuckled. "Well, now you know what *doesn't* work. Here's what my dad did. He started researching how people change and grow. I introduced him to the work of a woman named Kathie Dannemiller. I became familiar with her work in college. Dannemiller created a unified theory of growth that went something like this. Change (equals) Dissatisfaction with the status quo (times) a vision for what is possible (times) a first, concrete step toward the vision. If these are greater than the resistance, then you will have change and growth." Bob took out a 3x5 card and began to write. "So, her formula was $C = D \times V \times F > R$.

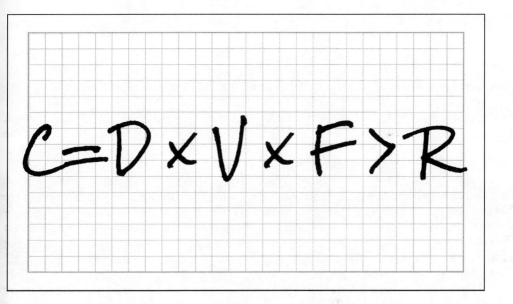

$$C = D \times V \times F > R$$

Because Dissatisfaction, Vision and First Steps are multipliers, if any one of them is absent, the sum will be zero and no growth or change will occur. A believer can be dissatisfied and have a vision for what's possible, but if they don't have a first concrete step they can take, nothing happens. A person can have dissatisfaction, vision, and a first clear step to take but if the resistance of time, location, people or money is greater, still nothing happens. I don't think he ever told anyone, but he was careful to follow that formula in his preaching...addressing dissatisfaction, vision, first steps and potential blockers."

"I've never heard anything like that before," said Tom, taking the card from Bob. "I mean it sounds so secular."

"Well, it doesn't stop there. I also introduced Dad to the work of Albert Bandura, professor emeritus at Stanford. The guy is still active at 94 and is recognized as the world's greatest living psychologist. His theory on growth is that before anyone begins any behavioral change, they have to be convinced of two things. First that they could do it. He called that 'efficacy' and second, that if they did it, it would be worth it. So, think of it this way, whenever people give up on a growth journey...to get in shape, lose weight, save money, graduate from college, practice spiritual disciplines and the like, it's because they believe that they either can't do it or even if they did it, it wouldn't be worth it. So, Dad worked that concept into his toolbox of growth—helping people understand that they could change and then painting a picture of what life would look like on the other side of growth."

"That sounds interesting Bob. I love the concepts. I just wish they came from the Bible," said Tom.

"Well, as Solomon said," mused Bob. "Sometimes even the lowly ant can give you wisdom and insight."

In the bottom of the sixth inning the Rockies started their comeback with Trevor Story's crushing home run deep into left field. The inning ended with the score tied, 2-2.

"Dad was also influenced by Andy Stanley and North Point's approach to discipleship," said Bob.

"What's Andy's approach?" asked Tom.

"Andy says everything he learned about discipleship he learned as a youth minister. He saw that kids that were growing and becoming disciples shared five things in common. I don't remember all of them, but it was something about practical teaching, a providential relationship and the like. The point is Andy used a data-informed approach. Data tells the story of how we got to 'now.' So once Andy learned what elements were most influential in making disciples, he intentionally formed discipleship journeys around those five things to influence what might happen going forward."

"That makes a lot of sense," said Tom. "So, your dad adopted Andy Stanley's five things?"

"No, he didn't but he used Stanley's approach as a scientist. He used reverse engineering. He interviewed about forty or so people in his church who seemed to be walking with the Lord and making a kingdom impact and then looked for commonalities in their experiences, habits or relationships. By the way, reverse engineering is a great way to discover the common characteristics of your best givers, your best leaders, your best volunteers, etc.," said Bob. "What are they doing that the half-hearted don't do?"

Tom thoughtfully nodded his head. The wheels were beginning to turn. "Well, what did your dad discover?"

"Actually, there were a bunch of things he discovered," Bob said, "and I could text him to find out, but the one thing I do remember is that growing Christians were those who were simply saying 'yes' to Jesus. That was their growth journey. As long as they were responding affirmatively to the Lord, they were growing. Dad learned a lot from that, and it affected how he ended his sermons by defining clear steps a person could take to move from 'hearer' to 'doer.' He created more opportunities simply to say 'yes.'"

It was like drinking from a fire hydrant for Tom. So many new ideas were firing in his brain. "Dang, that was challenging Bob. I didn't get this in seminary. That stuff on growth has given me so much to think about."

By the time of the seventh inning stretch the game was still tied 2-2. As the temperature dropped both Bob and Tom had put on their winter jackets and pulled their winter hats over their ears. Tom made certain his winter hat fit over his Astros cap. A carpet of peanut shells lay at their feet. Tom didn't want the game to end without hearing about the fifth motion. "So, we've talked about attract, get, keep and grow...which are really helpful. What's the last part of...what did you call it...the operating system?"

Bob knew he had saved the best for last. "Multiply."

"Multiply what?" asked Tom, zipping up his parka.

"These are the people who actually *multiply* the mission of your church through their giving, their serving—either inside or outside the walls, through their leading small groups or ministries, through their inviting, evangelizing, discipling and advocating for the church. My dad calls these folks 'engaged believers' because they are engaged in fulfilling the God-given mission of the church." Bob paused for a minute to let his words sink in before continuing. "And multipliers are *qualitatively* different from the first four movements because as good as the first four movements are to the framework, they are all about *consumption*. Multiply is about *contribution*. So, there is a very big difference between one who is multiplying the mission and one who is a very active consumer. An active consumer might be someone who attends the weekend service 52 weeks a year, is in a couple of small groups, and faithfully goes on the men's retreat every fall. All these are consumptive activities. And..." Bob paused for effect, "every consumptive activity has a law of diminishing returns attached to it beginning from day one."

"What do you mean...'law of diminishing returns?'" asked Tom.

"Have you and Amy ever been to an 'all-inclusive' resort?" replied Bob.

"Yeah, about a year ago Amy and I went down to Playa Borracho outside of Cancun and had a great time."

"I'll bet it went something like this...the first night you could hardly believe your eyes, prime rib, lobster tail, crab legs...and those pastries and breads and all those amazing Mexican dishes and desserts. If your first meal in heaven was like this, you would not be disappointed. But I'll bet around night five or six you and Amy skipped dinner and slipped off into town just to get some street tacos or maybe a bowl of Aztec Soup."

"How'd ya know?"

"Because every consumptive activity has a law of diminishing returns attached to it...no matter how good the activity is. I have a buddy about my age, who landed an incredible job at a law firm here in town. His job was simply to entertain the firm's clients. So, he was given pretty much an unlimited budget for sports and concert tickets. I mean we're talking Broncos, Rockies, Avs, Elton John, Adele, Lady Gaga, the Stones...anyone who came to town. He had an unrestricted expense account for taking clients to dinner—Elway's Steakhouse, Denver Chop House...you name it. And of course, cigars, liquor...whatever. He was a scratch golfer so now could golf any time he wanted, as much as he wanted, at any course he wanted as long as he had a client with him. He had come out of church work so this was quite a switch and he absolutely loved it...for the first three or four months, and of course was the envy of all his ministry buddies."

"I'm envious now," said Tom.

"Well hold on. Within two years, he left that dream job and started a nonprofit that's now impacting hundreds of thousands of people around the world and is absolutely loving it," said Bob.

"Wait...what?"

"Well, it seems God designed us to be more fulfilled by contribution than consumption. I assume you feel that way...that you are more fulfilled by preaching than by listening to another preacher."

Tom nodded.

"So, don't be fooled by first time visitors who come up to you, fawning over you. 'Oh pastor...your message this morning just spoke to my heart. It was so good,' because unless they figure out a way to contribute to the mission, they'll grow as tired of you as you grew of the *chilaquiles* in Mexico or as Dave did with Rockies baseball. I think it's an irrefutable law...our need to contribute, but I think most pastors are blind to it. Most are just happy when folks show up and listen to their sermons."

"I guess that explains why Amy says the best part of our Mexican vacation was the cooking class she took. She came back all bubbly, talking about what foods she would prepare once she got back home. And I have to say she's gotten really good at cooking *estillo mejicano*, as she likes to say."

Bob rubbed his eyes. "I don't know about you but, if I had the talent...and was twenty-two again, I think I'd be more fulfilled being on the field playing tonight than sitting in the stands watching others play. Some of my best memories were playing Little League and later in High School. We were CIF champions my senior year. Dang that was so much fun. So, one of the problems you need to solve for is helping every person at Daybreak Church, from children to senior adults, multiply the God-given mission of your church," said Bob dropping his empty peanut bag to the deck. "Help them move from consumers of religious goods and services to being active contributors to the mission...from members who expect privileges to partners who help fulfill the mission. That's what really matters."

"I've never heard this before Bob. Thank-you," said Tom.

Bob reached into his pocket and pulled out a 3x5 card, wrote down a couple of words and handed the card to Tom. "Here's a good reminder."

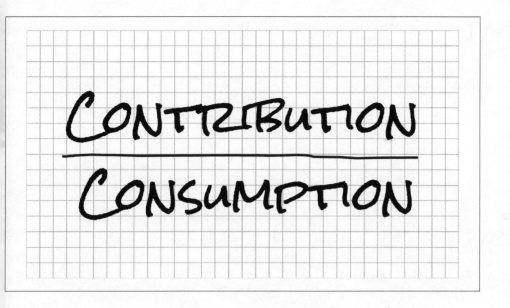

CONTRIBUTION
CONSUMPTION

Tom stared at the card. "Yeah, contribution over consumption."

By the bottom of the 9th the game was still tied at 2-2. This game would see extra innings which created space for one more thoughtful question from Bob. "Do you have any idea how people hear about your church, or why they decide to check you out by attending? And why do they stay, grow and contribute?"

"Well, I've just been here six or seven months now and uh...I..." said Tom hesitantly.

"Well, you could just ask your congregants through a short survey. It's the simplest way to find out," said Bob.

"I'd have to check with the elders of course but I could try..." Tom started.

Bob cut him short. "As my wise mentor Yoda says, 'Do or do not. There is no try.'"

"Okay, I'll check with the elders," said Tom.

Bob pulled another 3x5 card from his back pocket and in block letters wrote:

ATTRACT-GET-KEEP-GROW-MULTIPLY

Then he handed the card to Tom. "AGKGM...'All God's Kids Got Mojo'—AGKGM...Attract, Get, Keep, Grow, Multiply—"All God's Kid's Got Mojo." That's how my dad taught the framework. Hand me that card back, would you? I need to give you two more words. And on these seven words you can build your entire ministry."

Tom handed the 3x5 back to Bob and Bob wrote two words below his five-word framework. He carefully wrote the two words:

KNOW & MATCH

"There's your job description Tom," said Bob.

Tom looked down at his card. My job in seven words, he pondered.

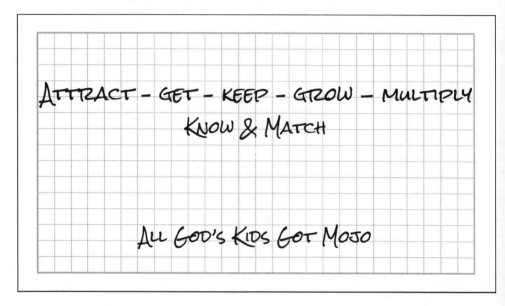

Tom put the card into his back pocket.

In the twelfth inning, Phil Gosselin scored off of a Bryce Harper double to put the Phillies up 3-2 going into the bottom of the twelfth inning. It was do or die time. With two outs and Tony Wolters stranded on first base, Charlie Blackmon stepped up to the plate and cranked one over the right-centerfield fence for a walk-off home run to win the game. Bob and Tom high-fived each other. "Glad we stuck around. Not often you see a walk-off homer," said Tom. It was after 11 pm when the game ended and both men headed for home. The April night air was chilly as Tom left the stadium and headed towards home. But it had been an especially good evening and Tom was looking forward to what was coming. Contribution over consumption...All God's Kids Got Mojo and he had new mojo tonight. Hmmph...my job in seven words, he pondered.

Tom walked home, thinking about all he and Bob had talked about. They covered a lot of ground in the past four and a half hours, and this was all so new to him. The Church Engagement Framework, he thought. Yes, that's what I need to solve for. That's my job alright.

Amy had gone to bed, but Riley greeted him at the door as was her habit. Tom leaned down and scratching her behind both ears said, "You won't believe what I learned tonight."

Chapter four

At church

Tom's message on Nehemiah 3 went surprisingly well for having so little meaningful text to work with. Tom focused on Nehemiah's emphasis on rebuilding the gates of the city walls. There was the fish gate, the horse gate, the sheep gate, the water gate, the fountain gate, the valley gate, the east gate and even the dung gate. Each gate served a specific purpose that led to the flourishing of Jerusalem. "Gates are for letting good, life-giving things into your life and for keeping bad, evil and harmful things, out of our lives. And you're the gatekeeper," Tom had said. The Legacy service was over. Harold had left half-way through Tom's message. What was he up to? Tom wondered.

Before Tom started pastoring at Daybreak Church, the elders had named the nine o'clock gathering "Legacy"—meaning "something handed down from the past" and the 11am service "Contemporary"—from the Latin word meaning "with the times." The Legacy service was an hour-long snapshot of what church had been like for the septuagenarians during their most formative spiritual years in the 70's. It was a trip down memory lane— "The Old Rugged Cross," "Sweet Hour of Prayer," "Come Thou Fount of Every Blessing," and so forth. Henry Parker, in his early 80s, approached Tom after the first service.

"How are you this morning Henry?" asked Tom.

"I'm drinking from the saucer because my cup runneth over Pastor," said Henry with a twinkle in his eye. "That was a good sermon this morning young man. Say, have you given any more thought to bringing back "Sip and Sing" on Sunday evenings? I think it is the key to getting young people back in the church. The Fellowship Hall was packed every Sunday night and young people were getting saved every week. It was wonderful. By the way the Gaithers Homecoming is on TBN tonight at 6. You don't want to miss them Tom. Junior Sample and Lulu Roman are going to sing a duet!"

"I'll give it some thought Henry. Good to see you and Pluma here this morning."

Before returning to his office Tom stopped by the two adult Sunday School classes, stuck his head in to say hi and then made his way towards the youth center where Tanika, the Minister to Students, had put out an ice-breaker question in a game she called "Five by Five."

"What would it be like if the 17-year-old Jesus played for your high school football team. OK, count off by fives and get into groups...you guys know the drill. You've got five minutes to answer the question using verses from the Bible to justify your answers. Now go!" Tom thought Tanika was a great hire. Just hope we can keep her around for a few years.

At church in the all-hands staff meeting

At Monday's all-hands meeting Tom skipped his devotional and got down to the project he was most excited about. After explaining the Church Engagement Framework, their "operating system," Tom divided the staff into three groups and handed them each team a large sticky poster and asked each team to fill out Daybreak's "report card." After 30 minutes of robust debating each team presented their findings. They could define the "win" and for the most part knew where they presently stood, as defined by the grade they had given themselves. They just weren't sure how to get from where they were to where they wanted to be or which area they should work on first.

Operating System	Grade	What does 'winning' look like?	How do we get from where we are to our win?
ATTRACT Ability to make others know we exist			
GET Ability to get people in the door for the first time			
KEEP Ability to return visitors			
GROW Ability to grow disciples in our growth model			
MULTIPLY Ability to develop leaders who x the mission			

"I'll be the first to admit that I'm not certain of the way forward either. But I am confident we'll discover a process that will give us a place to begin and a way to measure going forward," said Tom.

Reflecting on Bob's insight that people are more fulfilled by contribution than consumption, Tom said that from this point forward, he would no longer be giving the staff devotionals, but each staff would trade off going forward. "You remember five percent of what you hear but 100 percent of what you teach, so this will be part of your staff development," said Tom. Surprisingly, the staff seemed enthusiastic about this change. Later in the day he called Harold to suggest that elders also lead the devotions before the elder meetings. Harold sighed but complied.

At the elder meeting

It was the last Tuesday in April and Harold started the elder meeting punctually at 7pm. After the reading and approval of the minutes from March's meeting, elder Gene Poole gave the devotional on "Fixing our Eyes on Jesus," though to Tom, it sounded more like 'fixing our eyes on cheeses,' which caused Tom to smile. Harold then reviewed the declining month-over-month numbers around attendance and giving with the precision of an accountant.

"Easter gave us a slight bump in attendance but now we're coming into the summer months which traditionally are lower than any other time of the year." Harold looked at Tom as if to say, "It's all on you buddy," although he would never actually call anyone "Buddy."

Breaking the silence Tom spoke. "Thanks, Harold, for such a thorough report. I think the way forward is to first get an idea of what got us to where we currently are. I'd like to suggest that we take a short assessment to get an idea of how our people heard about Daybreak and why they decided to come for the first time, why they stay here, how they are growing, etc. This way we can build on the positive things we know have worked in the past." Although Tom was at every elder meeting, he had a non-voting position so the most he could do is make a proposal, cross his fingers, pray and hope for the best.

Harold took the high ground by framing the moment. "Tom, I know you think this is a good idea but that's not how we do things around here. For over forty years, Pastor Arnie never asked anyone what he should be doing to lead this church. He listened to God. and God listened to him. He was a man of prayer. Twice a year he would go up to the mountains and seek the Lord and always come back with a God-given plan. He grew the church to over two thousand. We need men of God to lead us…not survey takers. Jesus never asked people what he should do and neither did Pastor Arnie…and neither should you."

Dang! thought Tom reflexively. "God help me," he found himself praying. And God sort of showed up. "I can never replace Pastor Arnie…that's for sure but you knew who you were getting when you agreed to let me lead this church." He tried to measure his words. "I think Jesus himself was always taking short assessments and then acting upon how people answered. Jesus asked, 'What is it that you want?' with most everybody. Seems to me he responded to what he knew about people. And as much as I want to be like Jesus, I don't have the ability to know what's on people's minds, so asking the people through a short survey seems to be a good first step and afterwards, I can share the results with the elders." Tom could see most heads nodding like bobbleheads in agreement. That came out better than I thought, he found himself thinking. Harold frowned. He may have lost this skirmish, but he would win the war.

"Tom, you have five months to put this church back on track."

"That's all the time I need," said Tom. He had safely gotten to first base.

Tom had the approval of the elders to move forward. Striping the parking lot was put off for discussion until next September. After closing in prayer, Harold nodded to the group, careful not to catch Tom's eye, and slipped into the night.

At home
By 8:50 pm Tom was parking his Honda in the underground parking at the Douglas Apartments and walked up the stairs to his condo. Amy was still up when Tom stepped through the door. "How was the elder meeting?"

"I don't know what I did to get on the bad side of Harold, but that guy is out to see that I fail, and all the elders just follow him like sheep. But I did get their approval in taking a short congregational survey."

Amy reached out to take Tom's hand. They may not have had a perfect marriage, but they were good people who tried to improve. "Skip your men's group tomorrow night and let's go out to dinner. It'll give us a good time to re-connect."

"That sounds tempting but what kind of example would that set?" asked Tom. How about Wednesday...no that's our small group. We'll figure it out Amy. How about lunch on Friday?"

Friday was Tom's official full day off so after lunch with Amy, he fixed himself a cup of coffee and as an afterthought reached into his back pocket and found the 3x5 card Bob had given him a couple weeks before. I suppose I could wash these jeans a bit more often, he thought.

ATTRACT-GET-KEEP-GROW-MULTIPY
KNOW & MATCH

As Tom stared at the card and the card started to speak to Tom. Attract who? Get who? Keep who? Tom's mind started racing... He moved out of the kitchen into the spare bedroom-office, found his own 3x5 note cards and started writing.
Attract...the city
Get...the curious
Keep...the visitors
Grow...the motivated
Multiply...disciples...the contributors to the mission...fellow laborers!

Tom started sketching. How can I visualize this? he thought. First, he drew concentric circles with "Multiply" as the bullseye. He turned the card over and drew a triangle with five levels with "Multiply" occupying the apex of the triangle. No, that wasn't the visual either. What had Bob called these? Tom thought hard. "Motions!" That's what Bob called them. I've got to have motion. He reached for a fresh note card and drew five columns with a gap between each column. And in those gaps, he drew an arrow. Something's got to happen here, in the gap, that moves people to the next motion, he thought.

Fourteen Fridays - 37

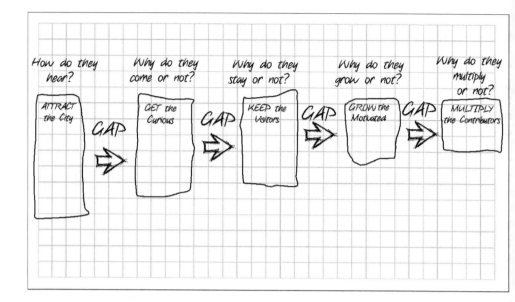

There it was. That's my framework...that's my job. He looked at the card one more time before slipping it into his back pocket. It had only taken him twenty minutes to have a visual of his task ahead.

Friday, May 3. Colorado Rockies v. Arizona Diamondbacks

"I'm off to the game Babe...See you when I get home!" Tom was out the door. Walking the couple blocks to Coors Field, with excitement Tom anticipated his conversation with Bob. He had the same feeling that he had when he discovered an insight from Bible study. Whether the feeling came from the Holy Spirit or from a surge of dopamine, it didn't matter. It always felt great to discover something new.

Tom arrived early enough to buy his usual steak and potato burrito. At five bucks and a dollar for a water, it was a cheap dinner. And why not buy a couple of bags of peanuts— one for him and one for Bob.

It was the first Friday in May and the Diamondbacks brought some of their warm Arizona weather with them. T.S. Eliot had said that "April was the cruelest month" and it had been just that for the Rockies, entering May with a 13-17 record. And it had been a cruel month for Tom. The weather had been cold all week with Denver temperatures touching the freezing level three nights that week, but this evening was close to 70 when Bob nudged Tom to signal that he was coming into the row. Tom stood up to let Bob pass and smiled as he read the words on his T-shirt as he passed by.

"THERE'S NO KNOWLEDGE IN THE ROOM, ONLY HYPOTHESES THAT NEED TO BE TESTED IN THE STREETS." STEVE BLANK

"Tell me about your T-shirt," said Tom. "What the heck does that mean?"

"It's one of my favorite quotes by Steve Blank, who is basically a guru on start-up businesses. It's just a reminder that no matter how good an idea seems to us...how inspired we might feel...how right we think we are...the best we have is a hypothesis. So that hypothesis needs to be tested in the streets. So, Blank's admonition is always, 'Get out of the building!'"

"I'm not sure that really applies to church work," Tom pushed back.

"But you really don't know if it does or not," Bob smiled.

The Rockies took to the field as Diamondback's Tyler Anderson threw his warm-up pitches. Anderson played his college ball for the University of Oregon where he became the Ducks' all-time leader in strikeouts with 285.

Bob and Tom stood for the National Anthem and as the cheering of the thirty thousand fans softened, they took their seats.

Bob turned back to Tom. "How'd your elder meeting go?"

"It was the oddest elder meeting I'd ever been a part of," answered Tom. "It was a church discipline issue."

"Well, now you've got me. I didn't think churches still did that. What made it so odd?"

"This guy in our church was practicing sadomasochism," said Tom.

"Oh dear, what did you do?" Bob leaned in.

"We told him we'd have to bring him under the discipline of the elders."

"How did he respond?" asked Bob with increasing curiosity.

"Well... he LOVED it!" smiled Tom.

Bob paused and then couldn't stop laughing. "That's a good one...you had me there for a minute. But seriously how did your elder meeting go?"

"It went OK. I proposed asking the congregation about how they heard about the church, why they decided to visit and all that and I think I got approval to do so. I'm just not sure how to do it. It's a five-month fuse but I think the lead elder has already made up his mind about me," said Tom adjusting his Astros cap. "But I'll still give it my best shot. Who knows what we might learn?"

Rockies' pitcher Tyler Anderson quickly disposed of the first three Diamondbacks and the Diamondbacks pretty much returned the favor striking out three straight Rockies batters leaving Charlie Blackmon stranded on first base.

"Well, how did church go?" Bob asked.

"It was good...well, I know I enjoyed it."

"Right...I know you enjoyed it. I mean, has anyone but a senior pastor tweeted, 'SO PUMPED about the weekend service?' Ahh, but that's for another time." Bob enjoyed mentoring and training young leaders and he had learned the power that comes from simply initiating a conversation...if he thought he could help. "So, did you get a chance to think about All God's Kids Got Mojo?"

"Yeah, I did...and this afternoon I came up with a diagram that I think explains the framework really well," Tom caught himself. "I mean for me at least." Tom liked to think of himself as smart but liked to downplay his contribution to things, even when he thought it was brilliant. "Let another man praise you and not yourself. Proverbs 27:2" was branded into his thinking. With that he reached into his pocket, pulled out his note card and handed it to Bob.

Bob stared at Bob's five-column diagram. "Wow! This is good Tom.... Yea, I think this is a great visual of the framework. I like that you included gaps between each movement. Personally, it's been my experience that there is always a person in that gap who invites or challenges a person to take that next step both in business and church. I think that's what your survey will show but you'll have to see for yourselves. It's relationships that catalyze growth. My dad had a little formula: 'Content + Application x Relationship= Transformation.' Whenever you see change, there is usually a person in the gap. Yeah, this is excellent Tom."

As Tom basked in Bob's compliments he was interrupted by Bob's addendum. "You have also identified the largest part of your job as a leader."

"What do you mean, 'part of my job?'" asked Tom.

"Attract, Get, Keep, Grow and Multiply tell you *what* you need to do but it's the other two words I gave you—'Know and Match' that tell you *how* to do your job. In those seven words is your job."

Tom smiled at the simplicity of Bob's explanation of his complex job. "Tell me more about 'know and match.'"

Bob was in his sweet spot now. He was a teacher and a mentor but needed a starting point. "When Nehemiah's brother came back from Jerusalem, what were the first questions Nehemiah asked him?"

"Well, he said, 'Tell me about the city' and 'Tell me about the people.' I preached on this three weeks ago."

"And how did his brother answer?"

"Well, his brother told him that the walls of the city were torn down...the gates were burned with fire and the people living there were in great trouble and disgrace."

"And what happens next is what I really like about Nehemiah," said Bob. "Nehemiah didn't give a nod and say, 'Interesting.' No, he saw this data as *actionable*. And, as you know, the first half of Nehemiah is how he rebuilt the wall and the second half of the book is how he rebuilt the people...based on just those two data points. So, if you look at your framework, 'Attract' and 'Get' refer to knowing about the people in your city—people you *don't* have, while 'Keep,' 'Grow,' and 'Multiply' refer to knowing the people in your church—the people you *do* have."

"Why do you keep using the term 'data?'"

"Well, I personally think of data simply as 'the information leaders need to make better decisions in line with their mission.' What data do you have and what data do you need to attract, get, keep, grow and multiply? So many pastors see data as a point of illustration. Not Nehemiah...for him the data was the catalyst to action. And you already know the secret of making the most out of data," said Bob.

"I'm anything but a data guy, Bob," Tom protested. "I think I barely passed Statistics in college. It's just not my thing."

"But you are Tom," said Bob as he pulled out a 3x5 card and began writing. "If you're a preacher worth your salt you have mastered the process. You start with data—'What does the biblical text say?' Then you go to analytics—'What does the text mean?' At this point you might look at other data points—other passages to cross-reference until you have a clear understanding of what's being said. Then finally you move to application. 'If this is true, here's what we need to do about it.' You call it Observation, Interpretation and Application but in the data world it is Data, Analytics and Decisions. By the way...that's how Datanadec was named—by combining the first three letters of data, analytics and decision. It's the universal process that you've already mastered." Bob handed Tom the 3x5 card.

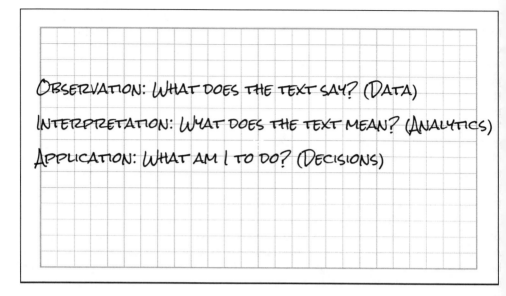

OBSERVATION: WHAT DOES THE TEXT SAY? (DATA)

INTERPRETATION: WHAT DOES THE TEXT MEAN? (ANALYTICS)

APPLICATION: WHAT AM I TO DO? (DECISIONS)

Bob had a way of identifying Tom's hidden qualities. It felt good to be around Bob.

"Here, let's look at your diagram again. Let me show you what I mean about the power to know and match. I think your ability to move people from one column to the next—Attract to Get, Get to Keep, etc. is based on 'knowing something about each group and then matching them to the next step God has for them. The more you *know* about the people in your city, the better you can *match* them to a message that might get them in the front door for the first time. The more you know about what visitors are looking for in a church, the better you can *match* them to what they are looking for... the next step God has for them. The more you *know* about people in your church the better you can *match* them to information, people and opportunities that take them to their next step in their growth journey. Data about your people helps you "know well the condition of your flocks." One size doesn't fit all," Bob said.

"But I can't adjust my message to every person," said Tom.

"No...but you probably can adjust your messaging and your programming to different *segments* of people. Segmentation seems to be the key to personalization. I think it's in 1Thessalonians where Paul writes something about warning those who are disruptive, encouraging the fainthearted, helping the weak. That's all about know and match. The more we know about people, the better we can match them to the right next actions to take. You don't help the disruptive and you don't rebuke the weak. Churches who are full of multipliers have mastered this know and match process."

Tom had a lot to think about. As he looked up at the scoreboard in deep center field, he found himself smiling...Hmph...know and match. He knew a little about how managers chose their lineups since he had coached a few Little League teams himself. The first batter was most likely the player with the highest on-base percentage. Your first four or five players were your best hitters and being early in the lineup, have more times to swing at the ball than players later in the lineup. Batting ninth was almost always reserved for the pitcher...typically the worst batter on the team. There it was...know and match. The more "data" a manager had on a player the better he could match that player to the place of greatest contribution. Tom hadn't unlocked the secret of the universe, but he was beginning to see the genius of know and match. The more I *know* about the people I'm trying to help, the better I can *match* them to something that will help them and maybe I'm not the one who has to give it to them. There are a lot of great resources out there. Pretty simple stuff.

By the bottom of the third the Diamondbacks were up 4-0. But thanks to the ability of Arenado, Desmond, Iannetta and Hampson to connect white ash to cowhide, by the bottom of the fourth inning the Rockies had it all tied up 4-4. Tom and Bob had bought a couple of beers and were cracking open the salted peanuts Tom had picked up outside the stadium.

Something Bob said kept returning to Tom's mind. "Hey Bob, what was it you said about segmentation being the key to customization. Segmenting who, customizing what?"

"It's basic stuff really," said Bob. "It ties in with messaging and how we reach different types of people. It's about sending the right message to the right person at the right time through the right channel. And all of these need to line up for the process to work."

"What do you mean?" asked Tom.

"Well think of Phillip's encounter with the Ethiopian eunuch. The Ethiopian was about to read a specific passage about Jesus in the scroll of Isaiah. At that moment the Spirit of God prompted Phillip to join the Ethiopian's chariot and Phillip asked the Ethiopian a question, 'Do you understand what you're reading?' in response to which the eunuch asked for help. A minute earlier or a minute later the Ethiopian would have been on a different passage but beginning with *that* passage, Phillip turned the conversation to Jesus, the Ethiopian was baptized and *Voila!* The birth of the African church. The right message to the right person, at the right time, through the right channel."

"That's a good one," said Tom.

"Different things motivate different types of people. Let's take introverts and extroverts for example. So, when you ask believers what they think heaven will be like, extroverts, like you and I, picture a place where we'll be in charge of ten cities, while the introverts might gravitate to Jesus' words about him going to prepare a place for them in his mansion. To those who have been struggling their whole lives to make ends meet, perhaps the words, 'Enter into your rest' are most attractive. I don't know exactly what heaven will be like but for get-it-done types, organizing hell seems preferable to sitting around in heaven in a hammock listening to choirs of angels. And the last thing an introvert would want would to be in charge of ruling over any city. So, I think the descriptions of heaven are broad enough to appeal to every personality type. Sort of like the love-languages. What's the love language of people you're trying to attract and get? In marketing, it is called a persona—a composite fictional character of the person you're trying to reach."

"Well, we want to reach everybody," protested Tom.

"Maybe...but perhaps the key to reaching everybody tomorrow is reaching the right people today. I mean though Jesus' mission was to redeem all of creation he strategically went after the lost sheep of Israel. The apostle Paul narrowed his focus to the Gentile population. So, if there is a person of a certain age, gender, marital status, income level, occupation or aspiration who comes to mind you have just created your first 'persona.' This is what Rick Warren and Bill Hybels did back in the 80's. For Rick Warren their persona's name was 'Saddleback Sam' and for Hybels it was "Unchurched Harry" and "Unchurched Mary"—the irreligious but curious people of their community. These were the personas they had in mind in their outreach and weekend services and they did see thousands come to faith. I think Saddleback had their 50,000th person baptized last year."

"But how do I choose one persona over another?" asked Tom.

"That's a really good question. I can only say what others have done. A megachurch pastor in the Phoenix area purposefully goes after the 40-year- old male because he's discovered that if the father is the first one to come to faith in a family there's a 93 percent chance that the wife and kids will also come to faith. But I think you can also build a case for going after millennials, Gen Z, children, young families. You've got to experiment to see what works in your church. By the way, your church already has a composite persona of who you are, so you could start there."

"What do you mean?" asked Tom.

"Social media advertisers like Facebook allow you to upload what's called 'a custom audience' of people in your church or a slice of people in your church...say just your millennial males, if it's a large enough population, to Facebook. Facebook then is able to form a persona based on demographics and interests of that audience segment. They then are able to identify people in your community who match the personas of those people in your church. Facebook calls this a 'Lookalike' audience and is able to send your targeted messaging just to these folks. It's quite effective. Because you most likely attract people who are like you even more than people you want to reach, this is a very important messaging feature of segmentation. Just Google how you might do that," said Bob nonchalantly.

Tom was struck by how little he really knew about things like Facebook advertising, but he was also confident somebody at Daybreak could figure it out.

By then end of the sixth inning the Rockies were down by just one run...7-6 going into the seventh inning.

Tom was thinking and then finally spoke. "Hey Bob. Let me buy you another beer and then tell me more about how those Facebook ads work," said Tom.

"Make it a Diet Coke and you got yourself a deal," said Bob.

Tom got the attention of the Soda Guy, held up two fingers and yelled out "Two Diet Cokes."

After Bob took his first sip, he put the plastic cup in the cupholder and began. "You probably have someone in your church that does this for a living, but the idea is super simple. Facebook allows you to send advertisements only to people you want to reach. So, you can send messages only to those who have "liked" your church's Facebook page. Or you can select the demographic characteristics or hobbies of people you're trying to reach. Or, as I said, you can upload the name and address of all the adults in your church and tell Facebook to create a 'Lookalike' audience composed of people in the community that share characteristics of people in your church. And here's the fun part, you can have some creative folks in your church create eight or ten different advertisements and run the ads for just one day and see which one most people click on. Then on day two, eliminate all the ads that were ineffective and continue this approach until the end of your campaign for a sermon series or special event, like Date Night. It's really cost-effective. A pastor friend of my dad did this and targeted only people within a geographic radius of his church who had 'liked' his church and got 90 new people in small groups that had never been in a small group before. And I think it cost him around $7 for each person who signed up. When you think that the average small group attendee gives $1,200 more per year than those who are not in a small group, it was a no-brainer. That's how Facebook generates revenue...around fifty-five billion dollars last year."

"It sounds kind of creepy that Facebook knows so much about us," said Tom.

"It's called target marketing and was pioneered by L.L. Bean back in 1912. Bean created a pair of waterproof hunting boots. He didn't want to send an ad to every household, so he got hold of a list of people who bought hunting licenses and sent advertisements only to those folks and started a nationwide mail-order business out of his brother's basement. The right message to the right person, through the right channel worked beautifully."

By the 7th inning stretch, the Diamondbacks had pulled ahead, 9-6 and Tom had more questions. "So how does Google work? How do they make their money?" asked Tom.

"Good question. Google's advertising model is the flipside of how Facebook works. Facebook ads come to you as you're looking at your Facebook feed. But we actually go to Google when we are searching for something. So, I'd say almost all your visitors have checked out Daybreak Church by searching Google. So, if this is the primary way, they find out about you, make sure your website is up-to-date and if your people can post reviews and photos, all the better. Because people who are searching for something on Google rarely go past page one to find what they want, ranking is super important," said Bob.

"Our website's pretty outdated. But don't companies have to pay a lot of money to show up at the top of a page?" asked Tom.

"That's right but there are a lot of ways to come out on top. So...let me type this in," Bob said. "Where...to get...married...in...Denver?" Bob scrolled though his phone. "Okay, I didn't find any church mentioned until the fourth page. So, you, or someone in your church could write an article titled "Where to get married in Denver" and most likely that article will be on the first page and you could take it from there. You can just go to YouTube to see how all this works. It's not that complicated and most likely someone in your church is really good at using Google. And I think Google still offers nonprofits...grants of something like $10,000 a month for AdWords."

"What...wait? $10,000? Well, you've given me a lot to think about Bob. I'll check it out and get somebody on it," said Tom.

By the time the Rockies went to the plate for the last time they were down by four runs—10-6. A good two-thirds of the crowd was still in the stands. They were seeing a lot of offense and for most of the crowd, there would be no work they had to get up for in the morning. The Rockies led off the bottom of the ninth with a single followed by Charlie Blackmon's home run over the Right-Center fence. Now the score was 10-8 and some fans who had left their seats now crowded the mezzanine to see what would happen next. Trevor Story took first base on a walk followed by Nolan Arenado who singled into short right center field. Story advanced to third. Daniel Murry walked to load the basis. David Dahl's single to first came with the cost of Murry being tossed out at second but also drove Story across home plate. Rockies were down by only one run with only one out and two men on base. They were poised for a great come-back victory. But fate and luck are unpredictable and Ian Desmond and Chris Iannetta both struck out to end the game.

Tom and Bob stood up, brushed the peanut shells off their laps. "See you next Friday? Padres are in town," asked Bob.

"Sure thing. Oh, by the way, do you mind giving me your phone number...in case I have any questions between the times we're together?" asked Tom.

"Sure. Hand me your phone and I'll send myself a text." Said Bob.

"OK...till Friday," Tom said.

"See ya Friday."

As Tom walked home that night, he kept thinking about what Bob had said. Reaching into his back pocket he pulled out the 3x5 card Bob had given him.

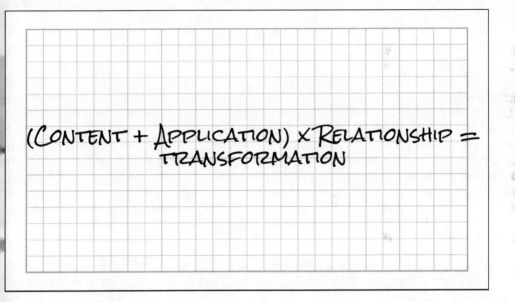

$$(CONTENT + APPLICATION) \times RELATIONSHIP = TRANSFORMATION$$

Tom unlocked the door and as entered announced, "Amy, I'm home. There's so much I want to tell you." Tom could hear Tucker Carlson's voice coming from the bedroom. There was Amy, fast asleep with the remote in her hand. "Well, I guess it can wait till tomorrow," he said softly.

Chapter five

Civic Center Park in downtown Denver

It was a beautiful Cinco de Mayo in Denver and Tom was anxious to get to Civic Center Park in downtown Denver after church and join the festivities with Amy. Houston hosted a decent parade on the 5th of May, but Tom was anxious to see how the Hispanic community in Denver threw a party. So as soon as Jerome had given the closing prayer, he was out the door and found Amy waiting in the car with the motor running and the air conditioning on high. He and Amy were not disappointed. Three hundred and fifty food vendors put forth their best Mexican cuisine. Two stages hosted continual live performances featuring mariachi bands, *baile folklorico*, *musica norteña,* salsa…you name it. And there was the low-rider car show, the taco eating contest and the chihuahua races. It was a great way to spend a Sunday afternoon getting to know their new city. On the way home Tom glanced towards Amy and said, "I know I've been really busy these past few months. I just wanted to thank you for being patient with me. You really lighten my load."

Amy took Tom's hand, "I had a good time too Tommy. If there ever were a relationship, I'd put up a fight for, its ours. And it's a good fight. But sometimes I just don't know how to get us unstuck."

At church in the all-hands staff meeting

"Let's get started…" said Tom looking at his notes. It was Monday morning all-hands meeting and he was running his own experiment to validate a new hypothesis about contribution. "Tanika, you're up."

The Director of Student Ministries responded. "Thank you, Pastor. My devotional this morning is from Proverbs 3:5,6. I've asked three of you to slowly read this passage from three different translations, The NIV, The Message and The Passion Translation. So maybe close your eyes to take it all in. Libby, why don't you start, then Elliot and Kaiya."

Libby looked down at her phone and she began reading slowly and thoughtfully. "From the NIV…

> 'Trust in the Lord with all your heart and lean not on your own understanding; in all your ways submit to him, and he will make your paths straight.'"

Elliot, the High School intern, was next. "Umm…this…is…from…the Message," forgetting that he was supposed to read the passage slowly…not just speak slowly overall. He looked at his iPad and continued,

> "Trust God from the bottom of your heart; don't try to figure out everything on your own. Listen for God's voice in everything you do, everywhere you go; he's the one who will keep you on track."

After an appropriate silence Kaiya, the new Middle School Director, opened her phone and said, "This is from the Passion Translation.

> 'Trust in the Lord completely, and do not rely on your own opinions. With all your heart, rely on him to guide you, and he will lead you in every decision you make. Become intimate with him in whatever you do, and he will lead you wherever you go."

Tanika gave a nodding approval to her readers. "Thank you…that was beautiful." Then she turned her attention to all fifteen of the staff. "Let's answer three questions from the passage. 'What do we learn about God?' 'What do we learn about people?' and 'What do we learn about God's plan for people?" What followed was a lively discussion where everyone brought something to the table. After quieting the staff, Tanika then asked each person, in light of what they learned to take one minute and write down one thing they wanted to stop, one thing they wanted to start and one thing they wanted to continue. When she noticed Tom did not pick up his pen she said with a smile. "That includes you too Pastor Tom."

"Oh, yeah of course," Tom said. It'd been quite some time since he had been in someone else's Bible study and actually asked to make an application. But Tom complied and actually was delighted with his answers and he felt he experienced a bit of the Holy Spirit in the process.

"Now pair up with someone and tell them out loud what you want to stop, start and continue," said Tanika. If it had been a long time since he had studied the Bible to benefit himself, it had even been longer since he shared an application. But he was in too deep to turn back now. Tom turned to Juan, who served as the Director of IT Services. Juan was a "Dreamer." Born in Guanajuato, Mexico, Juan's parents brought Juan across the border when Juan was three years old.

Tom began. "I want to start trusting God with *all* of my heart in *all* of my ways. I want to stop trusting the Lord with *part* of my heart in *some* of my ways. I want to continue letting God work his change process in me." And Tom felt that he really meant what he said.

"Is all that true Bro?" Juan asked.

A bit stunned by the direct question, Tom answered, "Well…yeah!"

"Just keeping it real Bro, ummm…a…Pastor. Here's mine…I want to stop looking at porn. I want to start a story-telling film project for our high school kids and I want to continue to rely on the Holy Spirit to change me to be more like Christ." With that he reached out and grabbed both of Tom's folded hands.

Wait…what…? thought Tom.

Fourteen Fridays - 49

Tanika finished her devotional asking for just "one word" from every person around the table. Tom couldn't help but notice the sincere sobriety of his staff in that moment. No one was checking their phones. A few people were dabbing their eyes. All of them had contributed and all of them had benefited. Tanika had hit a home run and Tom's hypothesis about "people being more fulfilled through contribution than consumption" was being validated. In 20 minutes, he had turned "what if..." into "what is." Tom decided it'd be a long time before he'd give a devotional in staff meeting again.

"Thank you Tanika for such a good start to a great week."

Friday, May 10. Colorado Rockies v. San Diego Padres
The Rockies' most consistent starter, German Márquez was on the mound, throwing the last of his warmup pitches when Tom sat down in his aisle seat. The Rockies would need their top talent to beat the Padres.

"Hey Bob. Good to see you. Here, I got you some peanuts," said Tom.

"Thanks Tom. Should be a good one tonight. I like that Manny Machado from the Padres."

Tom lowered his voice, "Hey Bob, did you see those two guys holding hands at the top of our section? Sickening! You could never get away with that at Minute Maid Park," said Tom adjusting his Astros' ball cap.

"I did see them, Tom," said Bob cracking his first peanut shell. "Just had a thought Tom. Do you personally know any gay people? I mean do you have any gay friends?"

"No way!" said Tom.

"Well, I think you probably do, and there are probably quite a few in your church. You just don't know they are gay," said Bob.

"Why would a gay person want to be in church Bob?" said Tom. "Have you forgotten about Romans 1?"

"Well, any type of sex never fills the God-vacuum. I mean you and Amy might have a great physical relationship but that doesn't erase your hunger to know God, does it?" Bob asked. "I think gays, or anyone else in the LGBTQ community can hunger for God as much as you or I do. Just sayin'..."

"Well, the gays are trying to ruin marriage," said Tom.

"I disagree with you on that one Tom. Seems to me that gays are the only ones fighting for marriage and the right to be married these days." Bob retorted.

Fourteen Fridays - 50

"Humph. I hadn't thought about that," said Tom. "But I still think homosexuality is a choice."

"Well, Jesus did say that some men are born eunuchs. And being born a eunuch is certainly a sexual condition and one they don't willfully choose," said Bob. "You know it wasn't until 1967 that inter-racial marriage was legal in all 50 states. And it wasn't too long ago that re-marriage after divorce was all but impossible."

"Ugh! I hadn't thought about that either," said Tom, pulling his Astros cap a bit further on his head. But Bob's thoughtful words gave him pause.

The San Diego Padres had strutted into Denver with a 21-18 record and were looking to sweep their National League West rival in this three-game stand. The mid-May temperatures had dropped to mid-March levels, but the sun would still be up for another two hours before melting into the horizon. All in all, it was a good night for baseball.

The first two innings were scoreless. The Padres pitcher, Eric Lauer was matching the prowess of German Márquez pitch for pitch. Eight batters down for Lauer and Márquez. This looked to be a defensive battle. But in the bottom of the third, Trevor Story stepped up and hit a crushing ball over the left-center fence, driving in Charlie Blackmon to give the Rockies a 2-0 cushion going into the fourth inning.

Tom handed a beer over to Bob. "Here, we need these to go with our peanuts. So, what's your t-shirt say today Bob?"

"I haven't worn this one in a while but it's pretty good." Bob unzipped his hoodie and turned towards Tom. The white letters stood out boldly against the black T-shirt.

FIRST PARTY
SECOND PARTY
THIRD PARTY
MY KIND OF PARTY!

"This T-shirt goes way back when the analytics team at Datanadec wanted everyone to become familiar with the basic three types of data...first, second and third-party data. So, we spent one Friday afternoon learning about these three types of data followed by a short party...well, cake and beer and some party hats."

"So, what's the difference between these types of data? Anything that can help me?"

"Oh yeah, because all three types of data help you know more about people you're helping to find faith in the city or know about people you're trying to grow in their faith in your church. The more you can know about people..."

Tom finished Bob's sentence. "The better I can match them to the next thing God has for them" he paused. "In the city and in the church."

Bob smiled. "That's exactly right Tom. So, you already know what first party data is—that would be the data you collect on your own people—name, address, gender, birthdays, names of their kids, email, phone, giving records and the like. Churches have been doing this...probably since the days of the early church. You can see attendance patterns, giving trends, baptisms, birthdays, anniversaries, small group involvement, who serves or volunteers. It's the easiest way to know and segment your people so you can serve them better—the whole 'know and match' thing. Because first party data is the data you collect, own and manage, it's also the most reliable of the three types of data."

"I guess I just didn't know what that kind of data was called. But it makes sense," said Tom. "But what do you do with that information?"

"My dad was really good at this. Along with the basic information, Dad also had the folks in his church indicate their occupations or professions and put that info in the church database. So, when he formed his data advisory board, he was able to hand-pick his team of seven really sharp men and women from the tech world whom he really wanted. And these data folks were over-the-moon in being asked. Now they have totally stepped up to help Dad grow into this area of ministry in using data and analytics to make better decisions. The magic of know and match again at work."

"Wait...what...a data advisory board? I suppose that's something I should look into," said Tom.

"Yeah, what's new and difficult for you is a breeze for many people in your church. And this helps them contribute to the mission of the church. One of the women on Dad's data advisory board took charge of digitizing all the prayer requests from the past 12 months and then used that data to form month-by-month word clouds that visualized the most common requests month over month. This was great first-party data," said Bob.

"What did she find out?" asked Tom.

"Well, the most common requests, across the board, were around marriage, relationships and family. The exception was for men under 35, whose most common request was for mentorship. Go figure. But in February the most common prayer request was around finances—bills, rent, mortgage payment...financial matters," said Bob. "Probably because people overspent at Christmas. But Dad used that first-party data to shape what he would regularly preach on or resources he'd bring into the church like Financial Peace University or monthly date nights. That's a great use of data."

"I think that's something I could do," said Tom.

"But it would be even better to have one of those data people in your church do it," said Bob.

"Oh, yeah, right," said Tom. "Yeah, contribution over consumption."

"A couple more things on first-party data," said Bob. "Assessments are really good for taking the pulse or temperature of your church at any given time and they are super-useful in measuring change and growth in your people over time. So, you could take a brief assessment before you began a class on finances or at the beginning of a growth journey, like a small group or Sunday School class and then the same assessment at the end of the class or the end of a growth initiative. Assessments like these not only measure an individual's growth but also measure the effectiveness of your initiatives or programs. If there is little or no life change, well...that's God's way of telling you to try a different approach. And you can make adjustments from there. A couple things we found helpful. First make sure the actual assessment questions are interesting, insightful and actionable and make sure you share the answers with the participants if you ever want them to take another assessment."

"I need to learn more about assessments," said Tom.

"Yeah, first-party data is pretty honest. I heard about one small groups pastor at a megachurch that was always boasting that 75 percent of adults were in small groups. After surveying over 7,000 adults, the data revealed that only 45 percent were in small groups. Of course, the small groups pastor protested that the data was wrong, but it is hard to argue with 7,000 assessments. Remember the story where Jesus heals the blind guy, and the Pharisees go to his parents to get some second-party data about their son? But the parents direct the Pharisees to go directly to the source...something like, 'He's of age. Ask him.'" First-party data is almost always the most reliable."

The bottom of the fourth inning was huge for the Rockies. Eight batters stepped up to the plate and made it safely on base. Seven of those touched home plate. Even the worst hitter on the team, pitching ace German Márquez slammed a double into deep centerfield that drove in two runs. By the time the carnage was cleared, the Rockies held a 9-0 lead going into the top of the fifth inning.

"What are the odds of a Padres comeback Bob?" asked Tom.

"Let me check," Bob said, as he reached for his phone. "Well, since 1957 there have been 330 games where the home team led by 9 runs and the home team ended up winning 327 of those games. So, I think it is safe to say we got this one in the bag."

Tom was thankful for Denver's huge lead as it gave him more time to drill down deeper with Bob. "So, I think I understand the value of first-party data. What do I need to know about second-party data that might be helpful?" Tom asked.

"Ah...second-party data...the red-haired, middle step-child of the data family. Not as reliable as first-party data and not as predictive as third-party data. I'd say the simplest way to define second-party data is that second-party data is simply someone else's first party data that you have access to or they are willing to share with you. So, if you've ever had your leaders take a Myers-Briggs assessment, a DISC test, REVEAL or an Enneagram personality test—the company does all the testing...that's second party data, and then they share the result with you. If you get on one of the demographic sites like census.gov or datausa.io there is a ton of demographic data, you can learn from that you have open access to—all for free I might add."

"Funny you should mention the DISC test," said Tom. When I was helping young pastors back in Houston, the church planting organization we partnered with gave the DISC test to every potential church planter. Of their over five-hundred successful church plants, I think I remember that all of them had a high D-I profile—'Dominant' and 'Influential.' And that's kind of funny as I think they found the best Bible study leaders were made up of 'S's and 'C's—the 'Steadies' and the 'Conscientious.' So, we concluded that our best Bible study or small group leaders weren't our best potential church planters. That saved us a ton of heartache, trouble and money. So, I think I could get my head around second-party data."

The Rockies held a comfortable lead, 9-2 going into the top of the sixth inning and Tom was anxious to learn more. It wasn't every day he could sit next to a person as knowledgeable as Bob for such a long stretch of time.

"So, what's up with third-party data Bob?" asked Tom before tossing a couple of freshly shelled peanuts into his mouth.

"Well...third-party data is useful in the sense that it can take in large amounts of information about what people have done in the past and then based on that data, can predict, with pretty good accuracy, what will happen in the future. It's what data people call 'predictive analytics.'"

"Wait... what?"

"Look at it this way Tom. Remember that passage where Jesus says something like, 'When you see a cloud rising in the west, immediately you say, 'It's going to rain,' and it does. And when the south wind blows, you say, 'It's going to be hot,' and it is.' That's how predictive analytics works. It's looking and learning from patterns in the past so we can predict what might happen in the future."

"I think I get it," said Tom slowly. "So where does all the data come from?"

"Most everything we do, everything we buy, every place we go, everything we search for on Google, every email we type, every text we send, everything we say to Alexa, everything we view on TV or the Internet, everything we buy with a credit card, every place we go when carrying a smartphone, along with every quiz or IQ test we take online and every 'like' and comment we make on Facebook leaves a digital trail of our lives. Companies that scoop up this data have over 5,000 data points on virtually every adult in the U.S. These data points create a psychographic profile for every adult—like whether we are introverts or extroverts, whether we like volunteer work or not, our interest in matters of faith. Third-party data is like an MRI—it can show you what's going on below the surface that first or second-party data alone can never show you. So, they say with Facebook, with just ten 'Likes' Facebook knows more about you than your co-workers. With something like seventy 'Likes'—Facebook knows more about you than your friends know about you and with over three-hundred 'Likes,' Facebook knows more about you than your spouse does."

"No!" protested Tom.

"Yes...this is how it works Tom," said Bob. "So, the predictive power of big data comes from looking at 'what people do next,' which creates a whole new field called 'predictive analytics.' Here's roughly how this works. 'People who are doing 'XYZ behavior' today were doing 'ABC' yesterday. So, we can say with a high degree of certainty that people who are doing 'ABC' behavior today will be doing 'XYZ' behavior tomorrow. Do you remember that story about Target and the 15-year-old girl?"

"I don't think so," said Tom.

"Well, back in 2012 Forbes magazine wrote an article about how Target knew a teenage girl was pregnant before the parents knew. It caused quite a stir, but it went something like this. An irate father marched into the local Target store in Minneapolis to complain that his 15-year-old daughter was getting advertisements in the mail for baby products, as if she were an expectant mother. 'Are you trying to encourage her to be sexually active?' he demanded. Well of course the manager apologized but a few weeks later it was the father who had to apologize. 'Apparently there were some activities going on that her mother and I didn't know about and she is indeed expecting...in August.' So how did Target know she was pregnant? Well, Target has a baby registry where moms-to-be can register and can enter their due date. In return they get a bunch of discounts and freebies. Well, Target tracks what these expecting women buy in each month of their pregnancy— unscented lotion, vitamin supplements, cotton balls etc. Well of course there is a whole other group of pregnant women who shop at target who do not register in the baby registry. But because they buy the same things, in roughly the same order as the hundreds of thousands of women who do register, Target is able to predict with 87 percent accuracy, not only that a woman is pregnant but also her due date, within a two-week window of accuracy."

"That's a bit creepy but I get it. I know that if I'm looking for something online...like shoes from Zappos or something on Amazon, I'll usually see a ton of ads for that product when I open my Facebook or am reading my news feed," said Tom. "And sometimes it's actually helpful. But what does freak me out a bit is when Amy and I are having a conversation about something random like vitamin supplements and then ads start popping up for vitamin supplements. It's like Alexa is listening in. I've heard that's not possible. What do you think Bob?"

"Well, you never know," Bob smiled. "So, basically first and second-party tells us about *what* people do. Third-party data can help us understand *why* people do what they do—motivations and aspirations. First and second-party data tells us about things we can see. Third-party data tells us about what we can't see. First and second-party data tell what happened. Third-party data tells what predictively will likely happen. First and second-party data tell you about people you have in your church. Third-party data tells you about people in your city—the people you don't have. Going off of the Church Engagement Framework, third-party data is super-helpful with Attract and Get, while first and second-party data really help you with Keep, Grow and Multiply."

"I think I'm starting to get it," said Tom.

"Well, the greatest insights come when we stitch first and second-party data with third-party data."

"How's that?" asked Tom.

"Remember Zacchaeus?" asked Bob.

"That wee little man," Tom sang. "Of course."

"We could learn a lot about him through first-party experience...through observation. He was a male, he was short, he was young and fit enough to climb a tree. Maybe we could tell from his dress that he was Jewish and maybe, because of his clothes, that he was wealthier than most. If we ventured into second-party data, others who knew him could tell us his name, his residence, his occupation, his position in the company, whether he owned a home or not and his net worth. But first and second-party data can tell us demographic information, but demographics alone don't give us the whole picture. They don't tell us the most important thing about Zacchaeus—'He wanted to see Jesus.' Third-party data shows us what observation alone can never tell us."

Demographics tell the "how much" in your community. Third party models tell the "why" of your community. Third party models, based on big data, have the ability to create propensity scores based on the *emotional drivers* of individuals. So, through the art and science of predictive analytics, pastors and church leaders have the ability now to see who is most receptive to the gospel, like who 'wants to see Jesus' or most receptive to become part of a faith community. Big data models can also tell us who has a high propensity to divorce, be addicted, to volunteer, to give, or even who is thinking about leaving your church, etc. Big data gives us the insight that demographics alone can never do," said Bob.

"Where can I get all this third-party data?" asked Tom.

"There's a great company in Boulder, that does all of this for you. Just look them up. They are helping thousands of churches better understand their cities...and their people," Bob said.

"I'll check 'em out," said Tom curiously.

By the 7th inning stretch the Rockies were still in command with a 9-2 lead over the Padres. The temperature was dropping so Tom took his woolen cap out of his coat pocket and pulled it snugly over his Astros cap.

"For it's one, two, three strikes you're out at the old ball game!" sang both Bob and Tom as they clinked their plastic cups and downed the last of their beer. Singing "Take me out to the ball game" was one of the last vestiges of public singing. More people sang this song half-way through the seventh inning than sang the National Anthem before the game began. Even all the men at Daybreak, who never opened their mouths to sing a worship song, heartily belted out this song at the top of their lungs.

"I think the church can learn something about singing from Major League Baseball," said Bob.

"What's that?" asked Tom.

"You can actually get everybody to stand and sing two times but probably not more than two times," said Bob.

Tom smiled at the connection Bob had made. "Good point." And men at my church say they are uncomfortable singing in public. Yea, I've got to think about that one, Tom thought to himself.

Bob turned to Tom. "Remember a few weeks ago, I asked you how people heard about your church, why they came for the first time, why they stayed and the rest?"

"Yeah, it was embarrassingly hard to answer. I just don't know," admitted Tom.

"Well, I don't want to be presumptuous, but your Dad did ask me to push you a little bit," said Bob.

"Just get to the point, would you?" said Tom. "I can take it."

"Every year my own dad took a simple assessment of his congregation. And from what he learned, he could practically map out his ministry priorities over the next several months. I took his survey and made a few changes and if you're up for it, it would be super-simple to give to your people," said Bob.

"Yeah...sure," said Tom. "Let me see it, will you?"

"It's about getting a little first party data." With that Bob pulled out a 5x7 card from his coat pocket and handed it to Tom.

Daybreak Church (DC) Three-Minute Survey

How long have you attended our church?	How often do you attend?	Which service do you normally attend?	Age	Gender	Relationship Status
Less than 1 year | 1-3 years	Weekly | 2-3x/month | Monthly		13-19 | 20-40	M | F	Single | Married
3-5 years | 5-10 years | 10 years +	A few times a year	9am 11am	41-60 | 60+		Divorced | Separated
					Children living at home?
					YES NO

How did you hear about Daybreak Church?

Why did you decide to attend?

Why do you stay?

What has caused you to grow?

How do you multiply the mission of Daybreak Church?
☐ Giving over $500 / year ☐ Leading a small group or ministry ☐ Serving inside DC or in the Community ☐ Inviting people to DC
☐ Evangelism ☐ Discipling others ☐ Other _____ ☐ None at this time
How many Daybreak services / messages did you watch online before attending in person
Are you generally satisfied with your spiritual growth and spiritual health over the past year? YES NO
Do you have at least one good and trusted friend at Daybreak Church? YES NO
In the past 6 months have you invited someone to Daybreak Church? YES NO
Have you had a "spiritual conversation" with a non-Christian in the past 6 months? YES NO
Have you had a meaningful conversation with one of Daybreak's pastors /staff in the past 3 months? YES NO
Do you have expertise in data, analytic or marketing YES NO

How likely are you to recommend Daybreak Church to your friends and colleagues?

0	1	2	3	4	5	6	7	8	9	10
Not likely at all										Extremely likely

"All of this is about Attract, Get, Keep, Grow and Multiply. Here's what I suggest...just print off a hundred copies and put them on 50 seats in each service this Sunday, tally the results and we can talk about what you learned a week from Friday at the Baltimore game," offered Bob.

"Why just a hundred surveys? Shouldn't we try to do this with all our attendees? I mean we are running close to a thousand?" asked Tom.

"This is a survey, not a census Tom. The idea is you don't have to drink the whole pot of soup to know what the soup tastes like. You don't have to dunk every Oreo to find out if Oreos get soggy in milk. One hundred is a good sample size for a population of a thousand that helps you be accurate without having to be precise. It'll be easy to tally at staff meeting without much trouble and statistically will be around 90 percent accurate. If you want to get to 95 percent accuracy, you'd need to survey almost 300 folks. I think a hundred will be fine and the results will give you an idea of what got you to where you are today and how you can build on what works, abandon things that don't work and experiment with things that might work." Bob answered.

This was such a new approach for Tom. "I got permission from the elders, so this is great. I'll give it a shot this Sunday. This is all new to me, so I hope I don't screw it up."

It was the bottom of the eighth inning when both Tom and Bob decided it was time to head to their respective homes. The Rockies had put two more runs on the board and had a statistically insurmountable lead. Tom was the first to stand up. "This has been really helpful Bob and I look forward to the next time we're together."

"Yeah, see you on the 24th against Baltimore," said Bob. With that Tom climbed the stairs towards the exit. He was home before 9:30 pm.

At home
"You won't believe what we're going to do on Sunday," said Tom as he came through the door.

"What's that, Tommy?" asked Amy.

"We're going to take a survey," said Tom.

"Sounds like a life-changer," replied Amy with a touch of sarcasm.

"Well...I mean it could be if we do it right," said Tom as he pulled the 3-minute survey out of his jacket and began to study the questions. Yeah, this'll work, he thought.

Chapter six

At church

Tom felt good about his Sunday message out of Nehemiah 4, which turned out to be a very rich passage personally for Tom. Nehemiah was fighting so many battles There were not only those rascals, Sanballat and Tobiah, plotting war against Nehemiah but internally his people who were building the wall were exhausted. What was it Bob had said to him? Something about problems being the obstacles to accomplishing your goals...no goals, no problems. And then there was Nehemiah's brilliant solution of the "both/and" against the opposing army. Half the men would work on the wall while the other half stood guard. And then they'd trade off. The rested guards would work on the wall and the tired workers would stand guard. Nehemiah was flexibly adjusting his tactics to fulfill his mission. Tom had a lot to learn from Nehemiah.

Tom had the 3-minute survey printed on a lightweight cardstock with the church logo prominently displayed in the lower right-hand corner. The survey was randomly placed on fifty seats in both services and during his welcome, Tom asked those who had surveys on their chairs to take a couple minutes to complete the survey and put it in the offering baskets when they passed by later in the service. Tom couldn't help but see Harold's glowering stare in response to Tom's announcement. There might be hell to pay but what the heck? Tom had to do something different if he wanted different results. And he did catch Amy's smile.

Tom was anxious to see the hand-written results of the survey so after the second service he went to his office to gather up and look through the cards. After a quick scan, he neatly stacked the surveys, put a rubber band around them, stuck them in his backpack along with his iPad and headed for home.

At church in the all-hands staff meeting

Tom was at the church by 9 am on Monday morning. For many pastors, Monday is their preferred day off, but Tom was of the persuasion (though he never told anyone) "why not give the church my tired day?" His all-hands meeting happened each Monday 10 am to noon or 1pm at the latest, but Tom wanted the extra time to think about how to get the most of his first survey and to print off some tabulation sheets.

After an opening prayer filled with a few too many "and Lord, we justs," Tom turned to Jim, the minister of missions and family minister. Jim and his wife Theresa had served with Wycliffe Bible translators for twenty-five years in Papua, New Guinea and when they left the field, Jim took the job as missions pastor at Daybreak. It was budget cuts and staff reduction that gave Jim his extra responsibilities with family ministry, but his heart was still in missions. Jim spoke from Luke 14 about the man who wanted to build a tower and the king who was considering going to war. Jim had done some calculations about the number of churches in the U.S. compared to the number of unreached people groups without any part of the Bible. He earnestly urged the staff, "We can do this. We can be the generation to fulfill the Great Commission." The devotional fell a bit flat, in Tom's opinion, but Jim was beaming about the contribution he had made, and for some of the younger staff, the Great Commission was a novel idea.

After the devotional, Tom gave instructions to the fifteen folks around the conference table on how they were to tabulate the results. First, they divided the cards by gender and tabulated the results. Then they divided the surveys by age groups—Gen Z, Millennials, Gen X and Boomers and Builders. After tabulating the results, they re-distributed the cards by length of attendance, frequency of attendance, patterns of giving, serving, leading, etc. Numbers were recorded and percentages crunched. Patterns were beginning to emerge and duly recorded. "Hey, I think Survey Monkey does all this automatically. If you'd like I can look into it if we ever do this again," offered Tanika, the energetic Director of Student Ministries.

"That'd be great Tanika. I just thought this first time we'd learn a lot just from tabulating the results by hand," he improvised. "Next time Survey Monkey for sure. But for now, is there anyone who can create some visuals of these results?"

After an awkward pause Tanika volunteered. "I'll take care of this, but I need your help. So, each of you take seven surveys...start passing them around. I'll create a Google Sheets doc right after staff meeting, with all the appropriate categories and you just enter your data and I'll convert all this to graphics and visuals. And please get this done today. Shouldn't take you more than 15 or 20 minutes," Tanika said with a winsome smile. "I should have something in your inbox by this evening."

Great hire, thought Tom. "Thanks, Tanika." As he looked at Tanika's smile, Bob's words came back to him...something about people being more fulfilled through contribution than consumption.

At home
After supper, Tom turned on the TV and spoke the words "Sports Center" into his remote and within a few seconds he was watching a recap of baseball highlights around the league. He looked at his phone and saw a new email from Tanika. The visuals were done. Tom got off the couch, walked into the spare bedroom and opened Tanika's email. There were the results. There was the dashboard. Tanika used two simple visuals to communicate the results of the survey—pie charts and bar charts. She used the pie charts to show the composition of the congregation—gender, age groups, years of attendance, frequency of attendance, how people heard about the church, why they decided to attend, stay and what they found most helpful in their spiritual journey. But the bar chart was where Tanika's work shone the brightest. In the bar charts she was able to show comparisons. The first thing that stood out to Tom was how much more satisfied congregants were with their spiritual progress who were serving and giving. There it was again...people are more fulfilled through contribution than consumption. There was so much here Tom thought and for the next forty minutes he studied the pie charts and bar

charts and his pulse quickened with anticipation at being with Bob on Friday night. He and Bob had a lot to talk about.

Friday, May 24. Colorado Rockies v. Baltimore Orioles

Tom folded his six sheets of paper, containing the dashboards, in half, then in thirds and slipped these papers into the right rear pocket of his jeans. He was anxious to get to the game and talk with Bob about what he had discovered about his church from one simple survey. They agreed to be in their seats around 6:00 pm, which would give them forty minutes before the first pitch was thrown. Tom was running a little late, so he regrettably didn't have time to get his steak and potato burrito. He'd grab a hotdog later.

"Hey, I got you some peanuts," said Bob as Tom was getting into his seat.

"Thanks man," said Tom as he adjusted his Astros ball cap and wedged the peanuts into his cup holder. After exchanging the usual pleasantries and catching up on life over the past couple weeks Tom was anxious to show Bob what he had learned. "The results of the survey were really interesting," said Tom as he reached into his back pocket and retrieved his dashboards. It's so interesting to see how many more boomers we have compared to millennials and Gen Zs. What I really found interesting is how people heard about our church. About 30 percent couldn't remember. And when it came to how people decided to come to Daybreak for the first time, something like eighty-eight percent came at the request of a friend. Don't you think it is interesting that…" continued Tom excitingly as he took Bob through every pie chart and bar graph colorfully coded on his six sheets of paper. "What do you think?" asked Tom, hinting for a bit of paternal approval.

Bob was impressed that Tom had followed through in such a systematic manner. "You did a super job Tom. This is great first-party data. I'm impressed by what you've done and that you communicated all of this using the two most common ways of displaying information—the pie chart and the bar chart. My friend Brian, who was a data analyst for twenty-five years with Proctor and Gamble, says that 'visualization is a tool of social persuasion,' and I think he's right. The right visualization serves as a compelling call to action, and it was Florence Nightingale who made the pie chart so popular as a tool of persuasion."

"Florence Nightingale, the nurse?" asked Tom.

"The very one…not just a nurse but she's really the founder of modern nursing based on what she did with data. In the 1850s the Brits were fighting against the Russians in the Crimean War. Florence was taking care of the wounded at a British Field Hospital somewhere in Turkey I believe. She was a statistician at heart and began recording the causes of deaths of the British soldiers each month of 1857. So, when she showed her 12-slice pie chart, it was clear that ten times the number of soldiers were dying of diseases than of battle wounds. Seeing the powerful pie chart convinced the British Army to totally revamp the hospital system. So, visualization is super-powerful as a tool of persuasion and a great way to tell a story."

"Yeah, I'm beginning to see that," said Tom. "Hey, another thing I found interesting is the question about being willing to recommend our church to friends and colleagues. I think we scored about seventy percent on this one. It would be interesting to see who the 30 percent are."

"Of all your questions, Tom, that last question is most determinative of where your church is going...but that's for a bit later," Bob said. "But I thought I'd introduce a new topic for tonight by showing you my T-shirt. The temperature had not reached 50 degrees that day, so Bob unzipped his black parka to reveal the wisdom of a printed T-shirt.

"INTERESTING" IS THE ENEMY OF "ACTIONABLE"

"What does that mean?" asked Tom.

"When most people come across research or statistics from the latest survey from big research companies, like Barna or Pew, whether it be the percentage of millennials who are not returning to church or the number of young Christian couples who live together before they get married or whatever, they universally say something like, 'Wow! That's really interesting,' and that's where it ends. Or maybe that statistic will be quoted in the weekend service as a shocking illustration of how our country is going to hell in a handbasket. The power of data is not found in illustration but found in analyzing that data in order to give us insight into an action we might take to get a different outcome."

"Now *that* is interesting!" Tom said awkwardly.

Bob smiled. "So, let's go back to one of the parables Jesus told about data...the parable of the lost sheep. When the shepherd counted his sheep and found that he only had ninety-nine sheep when he should have had a hundred, he didn't stroke his chin and say, 'Wow that's interesting. I used to have a hundred.' No instead that gap between what he had and what he should have compelled him to leave the ninety-nine and go after that one lost sheep. That's what we need...just like Nehemiah...enough data to give us insight into an action we can take to make things better. I've built my professional career helping people turn 'Wow!' into 'How' and that's where the fun is...creating hypotheses of what might make a difference and change the outcomes."

"Wow!" Tom found himself saying.

Bob smiled at the irony of the remark but gave Tom a "Well played" nod. "Let's look back at your data and see if I can show you what I mean. So here are your bar charts, comparing the level of people's satisfaction on their spiritual journey to their frequency of attendance, length of attendance, leading a small group, and these six or seven other factors. Anything you see here Tom?"

"Welllllllll," Tom said slowly, trying to buy some extra time. "It looks like the people who ranked the lowest in their spiritual growth satisfaction were also the people who checked 'none of the above at this time' when asked how they were contributing to the mission of the church...about 40 percent of our church checked that box."

"Do you think that's a causation or a correlation?" asked Bob.

"Well...I don't know. If I had to guess, I'd say it is more causation." Tom answered.

"How could you know with more certainty that you were right?

"Well, I suppose I could run some sort of experiment where these folks could actually be on mission with the church and then measure their satisfaction again...like the assessments you told me about," offered Tom.

"So you just noticed one of the most important discoveries....you don't *know* for sure so the best thing you can do is create a hypothesis and run an experiment." With that Bob pulled a 3x5 card out of his pocket and wrote the word "DATA." "Everything starts with data and data is a record of what happened or what is. But a single slice of data is normally quite useless until it's combined with more and more data until you can run some (and then he drew a curved arrow and wrote) 'ANALYTICS.'"

"Whoa. Slow down a bit. What do you mean, 'combine more and more data?'" asked Tom.

"Well, if I say '40' that means nothing to you. You know it's a number. Then I say, '40 degrees' and you know it's either a temperature or a latitude. Then I say, '40 degrees Celsius.' Now you know it's a temperature of 104 degrees Fahrenheit. Then I say, 'body temperature.' And you know that's abnormally high. And then I add, 'of my 7-month-old daughter,' you say, 'You better get that girl to the hospital...and quick!' You needed five pieces of data before the data became actionable," said Bob.

"I'm starting to see what you're saying," said Tom.

Bob continued. "So, analytics comes from comparing two or more bits of data until you can find some type of relationship, pattern or correlation. When you find that correlation, that is called 'insight.' Insights provide that sense of 'aha!' because you're starting to connect the dots." And Bob wrote out the word "INSIGHTS." "And when that moment occurs, your data has become 'actionable' because you can now create a hypothesis and run an experiment to test your hypothesis." Bob then wrote, "HYPOTHESIS." "Analytics can show a relationship but it is through testing and experimentation that you can see if there is causation—'Does doing this action cause this outcome?'" Bob then wrote "EXPERIMENT." Bob continued, "Data, analytics and insight come from past data. Your hypothesis and experiment results in new data that measures whether your hypothesis was true or not. It's about turning 'I bet' into 'I know.' And if your hypothesis on what you think would move the needle doesn't work, you create a different hypothesis and run a different experiment and keep doing this over and over again until you get the results you want." With that Bob filled out the diagram traced the figure-eight over and over again.

"Data, analytics, insights, hypothesis, experiment, new data...wash, rinse and repeat. We call this the 'Insight Engine' and this type of approach is called 'heuristics,' which is just a fancy word for trial and error. But eventually you're able to replace 'I bet' with 'I know.'"

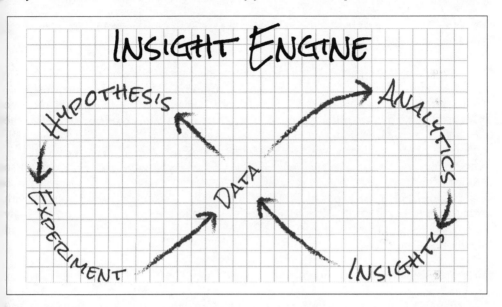

"But isn't that endorsing failure?" protested Tom.

"We are watching a game right now where failure is the norm. The best batters fail two out of three times for goodness sake. Nobody does it perfectly and yet everyone still gets to play. It's perseverance amidst failure that makes the game so interesting. I think you need to think a bit more like Thomas Edison. He experimented with thousands of fibers and spent tens of thousands of dollars trying to create a lightbulb that would burn continuously. When his critics called his experiments "failures" Edison responded... something like, 'I have not failed. I've just found 10,000 ways that won't work.' All of it is under the umbrella of what's called 'validated learning.' So, there is only success and validated learning. That's the way forward. Being wrong is the path to being right."

"I don't know Bob. This is God's work that he wants done, you'd think he would just show us the best way to get his work done. Moses went and met with God and God handed him the Ten Commandments...not ten experiments."

"My dad had a little plaque on his desk that read, 'It is the glory of God to conceal a matter but the glory of kings to search out a matter' from somewhere in Proverbs. When he was stuck, he would seek God...of course...but then try different things until he found what God had concealed. He called it 'Cosmic Hide-and-Seek,' but it's really how he said he drew closer to God. I think this verse explains why so many of the world's great scientists have been people of great faith; everyone from Isaac Newton who cracked the mystery of gravity to Francis Collins who cracked the mystery of the genome code. God hid something and people wanted to find it."

"Hmmm...." Tom said. "I hadn't thought of that verse in that way. But I think we ought to have more certainty."

"Certainty in our mission and clarity in our vision to be sure. But we need to be flexible in our approaches to accomplishing both," Bob said. "I think we need to move away from 'Thus saith the Lord' and move towards the Acts 15 model—'It seemed good to the Holy Spirit and to us that....' In other words, in view of what God wants done in this world, that we should try this...and if that doesn't work that we try something else until we accomplish what God wants done. Experiments are simply trying this and that on the way to accomplishing what God wants done. I also think when a leader uses words like, 'God told me....' then that type of language ends all discussion. I mean, who dares contradict God? Having a posture of experimentation invites input from others and as Linus Torvalds famously said, 'Given enough eyeballs, all bugs are shallow.'"

"Who's he?" asked Tom.

"He's a...uhh...never mind," said Bob. Just Google him.

The groundskeepers were raking the infield and chalking the batter's box when Bob thought of something he could add to the conversation regarding experimentation. "I have a friend named Bill who had a prolific career with Google over in Europe before moving to Boulder to work with a startup tech company. He was telling me that at Google they defined two types of problems—'complicated' problems and 'complex' problems. *Complicated* problems can be extremely difficult to solve but they have *known solutions*. So, if we had all the parts of your car's engine on the floor of your garage and were expected to build the engine...well, that would be a complicated problem. But with the right tools and an instruction manual, we could build that engine. It's just a matter of disciplined execution, you know...the grind of hard work. A *complex* problem is a problem for which there is *not a known solution* so the best thing we can do is create a hypothesis and run an experiment to see if it solves the problem. We can't treat complex problems as if they are merely complicated nor can we approach complicated problems as if they are complex problems. We just need to grind at the hard work of execution not experimentation. Our world is changing for sure. What used to work just doesn't work as well any longer. We can't just plug and play. And because we don't know with certainty what will work, we need to become experts in the process of coming up with hypotheses running experiments and measuring the results and doing that over and over again."

Tom looked at Bob. "All this is really new to me and if I seem resistant it's only because I'm trying hard to take this all in."

The preliminaries of the game were about to begin but there were three words Bob thought would be helpful to Tom on his journey. "A few years ago, I read a book by a guy named Eric Ries called *The Lean Startup* and later attended The Lean Startup Conference in San Francisco. A startup isn't just a smaller version of a big company. Ries says the purpose of a startup is not to make money or to get customers but is 'to find the sustainable business model before the money runs out.' He contrasted the old way of starting a business by creating a business plan, proforma charts, a pitch deck and all that as being obsolete and he points out that, with funding, someone could perfectly create a product or service that no one would want—which is exactly what Ries did in his first company. I think Ries' definition of a startup might interest you as one who helps church planters. Church plants are basically faith community startups. See if his definition resonates with you. Ries says, "a startup is a human institution designed to deliver a new product or service under conditions of extreme uncertainty."

Tom's eyes widened. "One more time…just a bit slower."

Bob slowly repeated himself and then poised his pen over the figure-eight diagram he had been working on. "Ries' three words he says all businesses are built on are…

BUILD-MEASURE-LEARN

…which fit nicely into the insight engine.

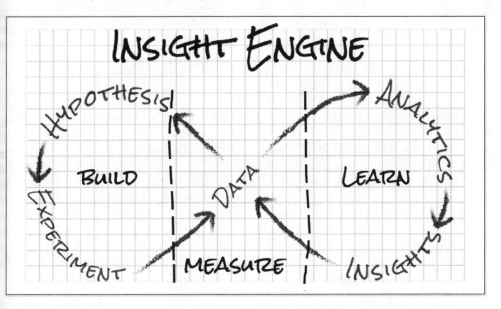

Similar to what we've been talking about, for Ries, it's about validated learning, repeating the build, measure, learn cycle over and over until we get the results we are looking for before we run out of startup capital. Ries is fond of quoting his mentor Steve Blank who says, 'There's no knowledge in the room, only hypotheses that need to be tested in the streets. So, get out of the building.' That's what was on my T-shirt a few weeks ago. I think as believers we get into that room, pray some, read our Bible some and then get one idea and quickly attribute that one idea as the thing God wants us to do. For Ries, it is about experimenting. If our experiment validates our hypothesis, we simply persevere towards getting results. If what we thought would work doesn't work, we pivot."

"What do you mean… 'pivot?'" asked Tom.

"Well like a pivot in Basketball, you keep one foot in place as you move the other foot around. So, a pivot is not a change in the vision or mission but a change in the tactic or strategy to get you there," said Bob.

"That is such a big idea. Say it one more time."

Bob repeated himself and took care to write it down on the backside of the card he had been drawing on.

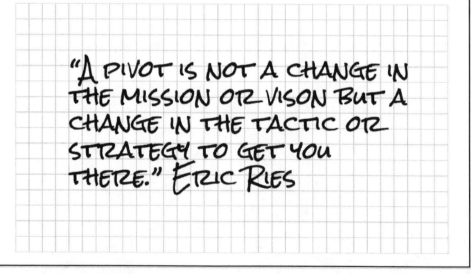

This way of thinking was all so new to Tom. They didn't come close to talking like this in seminary. But how helpful would this startup thinking be for his church planting friends. "A pivot is not a change in the mission or vision but a change in the tactic or strategy to get you there." Dang, that's good, he thought.

Tom and Bob stood for an enthusiastic rendition of the National Anthem. It was time to play ball. The Rockies drew first blood in the bottom of the first inning when Nolan Arenado drove the long ball over the fence along the left field line. Rockies 1, Orioles 0. - "Well, that's a comforting way to start the first inning," said Bob.

"What do you mean?" asked Tom.

"Well, statistically the team that scores first wins nearly 70% of the time," offered Bob. "So, I like our odds tonight. But you know data is not destiny and that's why the players play and hustle as if they have a 50-50 chance of winning...and maybe with more effort...more concentration...and a bit of luck the Orioles can turn this thing around. After all, a bat and ball have no memory." And by half-way through the fifth inning Bob's words proved prescient as the Orioles pitcher, John Means, was quickly disposing of Rockies batters. The hit-happy Orioles were leading 5-1 going into the bottom of the fifth inning.

Tom got up to grab a little dinner—a Rockies Dog with all the fixings and a Coors Light. Tom hadn't eaten a hot dog at home for years but there were few things tastier than a dog at a ballpark and the fans who would eat 1.2 million Rockies Dogs that year agreed with him. When Tom returned to his seat he said to Bob, "Hey I would have gotten you a beer but as you can see..."

"Yeah...yeah, you only have two hands, Bob feigned. "Hey, not to worry, I got one from the Beer Guy. Cheers!"

"Cheers! To a Rockies' win tonight."

"So, what's the odds of the Rockies making a comeback, Bob?" asked Tom.

"I looked it up while you were getting your hot dog. Since 1957 opposing teams that were up by four runs going into the bottom of the fourth inning ended up winning 88 percent of the time," said Bob.

But by the end of the fourth inning the Rockies had scored two runs and were back in the game.

"Hey, I remembered something that will be really important for you going forward," said Bob turning towards Tom.

"What's that?" asked Tom.

"You remember all that stuff about the Church Engagement Framework that we talked about?" asked Bob.

"Absolutely! All God's Kids Got Mojo," responded Tom. "Attract, Get, Keep, Grow and Multiply. That was super-helpful in helping me think of what we need to solve for. And then the 'know and match.' It is really clear what I need to do."

"Well, that's just it," said Bob. "When I said these are the five things you need to solve for, I didn't mean you alone had to do all the work."

"But isn't that my job?" asked Tom.

"Yes, but like any leader's job, you need to see that it gets done...it's not that you have to run all the experiments yourself. Here's what I mean. I have a pastor friend in San Francisco. We've talked a lot about Attract, Get, Keep, Grow and Multiply," said Bob. "Her church is around 500 or so but she has a lot of folks from the tech world who attend and are leaders in her church—people from Facebook, Google, Salesforce and the like who are used to solving complex problems through an experimental approach and validated learning. So, she has formed five different teams around Attract, Get, Keep, Grow and Multiply. Roughly, their goal is to attract more people to the church, get more people to an event or service, keep people coming back and prevent them from leaving, grow believers towards maturity and impact and multiply those who are multiplying the mission of the church. Each team runs two experiments every four months—so three experiments a year towards moving the needle in their given area. It's amazing what they are learning and how they are growing as they go through the Build, Measure, Learn process."

"Gee, but what exactly do they do?" asked Tom.

"Let me give you a simple graphic that should be really helpful going forward." With that Bob reached into his right back pocket and pulled out a 3x5 card and started drawing. "In the data world the Y axis always declares to the world what you're trying to solve for. So, for you, your Y represents a goal you're trying to achieve, a problem you're trying to solve or a question for which you're seeking an answer. And, by the way, unless you have a goal, problem or question, data can't be of any practical use to you."

"We have plenty of goals and plenty of problems...so keep going," urged Tom eagerly.

"Well, don't hide behind wandering generalities. The better you can define your problem with granular specificity, the more likely you are to come up with solid solutions that work. Remember what Einstein said about spending the first fifty-five minutes defining the problem," said Bob.

Bob continued. "Most likely for you and Daybreak Church your 'Y' is built around Attract, Get, Keep, Grow and Multiply—the five things every church must solve for. So, your 'Y' might be things like getting more first-time guests or increasing small group participation or enlisting more volunteers. Once you clarify your 'Why' ('Y'), the goal or problem you are solving for, you can begin creating your hypotheses of what will bring that about.

These hypotheses form the horizontal X axis. The X axis represents the actions you are taking that potentially affect the outcome of the problem you're solving. So, a hypothesis might be something like, 'If we did more of _____(X) we believe it would lead to more of this: _____(Y)."

"What might this look like for Daybreak Church?" asked Tom.

"Once you've clarified your 'Y'—the goal or the problem you're solving for, you can begin creating your hypotheses. Each experiment begins with a question like 'How can we increase first-time guests?' or 'How could we give every attendee a cross-cultural missions experience?' or maybe 'How can we reduce the friction of giving financially to the church?' or 'What can we do to help turn consumers into contributors?' 'Does small group involvement by itself result in spiritual growth?' Questions like that," said Bob. "But the more specifically you can identify your problem, the better chance you have of coming up with a solution. Then you run an experiment, based on your hypothesis to see if your hypothesis is correct. Did it move the needle? And you keep repeating that process until you have solved your problem. 'It is the glory of kings to search out a matter.'" Bob handed the card to Tom.

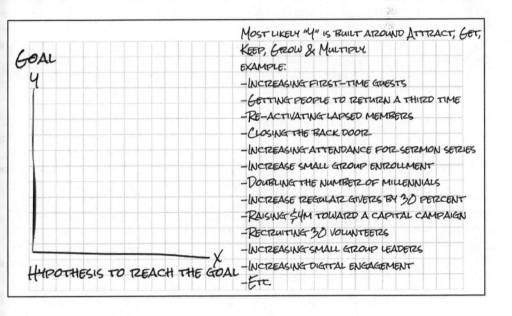

This is gold thought Tom.

"Oh...one more thing," said Bob. If you're a fan of the *Four Disciplines of Execution* and the concept of "lead measures" and "lag measures" you'll recognize the Y axis as your "lag measures" (the results you want towards your WIG—"Wildly Important Goal") and the X axis as your "lead measures" (the behaviors you do that affect the lag measures). If the lead measures (our actions) are not effective in producing the lag measures, then we have to adjust our actions and measure again until we find the behaviors that move the needle up and to the right. We act upon our lead measures and keep an eye on our lag measures and just build, measure and learn...build, measure, learn"

Going into the sixth inning, the Orioles were hanging onto their 5-3 lead.

"You sticking around to see how this one ends?" asked Bob.

"Oh yeah," said Tom. "I've got a feeling about this one. And the Rocks are within striking distance."

"Well, before we take off this evening do you mind if I give you a small assignment that we can talk about next week? Well, you've actually done the work, but I want you to look at it through new eyes. It's the last question in your survey," said Bob.

"I think we already talked about that one Bob...the one about the likeliness of recommending our church to friends and colleagues. I think we averaged close to a seven on that one so I'm pretty happy with that score...at least for now anyway."

"I'd like to teach you how to score it a bit differently and you'll end up with something called the 'Net Promoter Score,'" Bob said. According to *Harvard Business Review* it is the most important question any enterprise—business enterprise, nonprofit or church can ask because the answer is the clearest indicator of the future."

"Sounds fascinating. I'm all ears," said Tom curiously.

So, Monday at your staff meeting, go through your surveys another time and divide your congregants into three stacks. Those who scored you zero through six...those are your 'Net Detractors.' Those who scored you nine or ten are your 'Net Promoters.'"

"What do you do with the sevens and eights?" asked Tom.

"Just set them aside. They are your most apathetic, so they don't factor into the Net Promoter Score. We call those 'the passives.' It's a little tricky so I'll write it down on my card, so you'll remember.

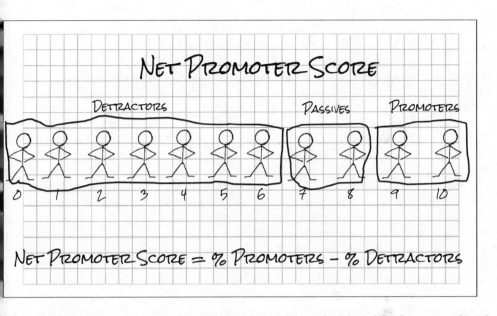

NET PROMOTER SCORE

DETRACTORS   PASSIVES   PROMOTERS

0 1 2 3 4 5 6 7 8 9 10

NET PROMOTER SCORE = % PROMOTERS − % DETRACTORS

So, out of your 100 surveys you have 40 promoters (9s and 10s) and 25 detractors (0-6s) and 35 passives, your Net Promoter Score (NPS) would 40 percent minus 25 percent for an NPS score of 15. With a hundred surveys your actual numbers will be the actual percentage so it should be fairly simple. So, at the Toronto game we'll talk about your Net Promoter Score. And I'd like you to do one more thing I think you'd find helpful. Once you have separated your surveys into piles, see if you can find three things your Net Promoters did that the Net Detractors didn't do. Then create a hypothesis on why there is a difference between the two groups and one experiment you could run to test your hypothesis."

"That sounds good," said Tom as he looked down at the Insight Engine and began tracing the rhythms of the figure-eight. "So," looking down at the figure-eight diagram Bob had drawn, "we start with data, move to analytics, then insight, then hypothesis, then an experiment where we get another slice of data...Build-Measure-Learn. Did I get it right?"

Bob smiled. "Then just rinse and repeat."

The sixth inning went by with just six batters stepping up to the plate—five strikeouts and one groundout. Retiring batters in succession cuts down on game time so the sixth inning flew by. In August of 1944 Boston Braves pitcher Red Barret pitched nine innings, facing 29 Cincinnati Reds batters (two more than the minimum of 27 batters). He surrendered two hits, walked no one, and struck out no one...averaging exactly two pitches per batter. The game lasted just one hour and fifteen minutes.

By the bottom of the seventh, Rockies' Trevor Story recorded his 100th career home run while Nolan Arenado smashed his 200th career home run down the left field line to tie the game at 6-6 going into the top of the eighth inning.

Bob looked towards Tom as they high fived one another after Arenado's home run. "Forget the stats. Forget history. We've got ourselves a ballgame."

It was nearly 10 pm when Rockies' Trevor Story stepped up to the plate and on a 2-2 count hit his 101st MLB career home run to deep right field to drive in pinch hitter Ryan McMahon across the plate to win the game in a two-run, walk-off home run. Story was greeted by teammates and an exploding bottle of champagne. Tom and Bob were on their feet slapping the hands of those around them as the fans cheered. "See you next week against the Blue Jays?" asked Tom.
"Absolutely!" said Bob.

Tom looked at the four 3x5 index cards Bob had given him before putting them into his back pocket. He had seen a great game and gotten quite an education that night. 'Build. Measure. Learn.' He had to remember that one.

At home
It was late when Tom got back home. Out of habit, as he entered the apartment, Tom whispered, "Honey, I'm home." For a moment he considered waking up Amy. His mind was racing with possibilities and he realized it wasn't near as fun having great ideas without the ability to share them with Amy. But he could share them with Riley. "Okay girl, on a scale of zero to ten, how likely are you to recommend Amy and me to your dog friends? What was that? A ten? Good girl."

Chapter seven

At church

Tom walked on stage and began his message on Nehemiah 5. It was a passage that began with justice for the poor of Jerusalem and ended with Nehemiah feeding a diverse crowd of 150 people, that included immigrants, every evening for supper. "Our gospel is not a Gnostic gospel. At Daybreak Church, we believe that the gospel has two wings—good news and good deeds and we need both of them to fly. The good news explains the good deeds, while the good deeds, validate the good news. This is why we started our backpack ministry that provides food for kids and their families on the weekends and during the summer. This is why we have our food drive in a couple weeks. It's why we raised money to give iPads to Denver Public Schools. There are over two thousand verses in the Bible that talk about ministry to the poor and that's what we are trying to do."

On the way out of the first service Harold caught up with Tom and pulled him aside. He was red-faced and wound tight. "Brother Tom, what you talked about this morning is a social gospel and Glenn Beck told real believers to run as fast as you can from a church that preaches a social gospel. Little wonder people are leaving this church. If this is your way of turning things around, you're on the wrong track." Tom was stunned but he believed in a robust gospel and preached from Nehemiah 5 even stronger in the second service. If he was to be fired for preaching the gospel...so be it.

In Boulder

Monday was Memorial Day. Summer was officially started, and Tom and Amy spent the day in Boulder with Amy's sister, Lucy and Lucy's family, jogging in Boulder's legendary 10k road race, hanging out at the Boulder Creek Festival and ending the day with a barbecue at Lucy and Brent's house. And Tom couldn't help but notice how thoughtful Brent was towards Lucy. It was hard to admit it, but there might be something he could learn from Brent and Lucy about improving his marriage.

At church in the all-hands staff meeting

The all-hands meeting had been moved to Tuesday so after catching up on what staff had done that weekend, Tom looked at Diana and nodded, signaling for Diana to start her devotional. Diana didn't need much direction. As the worship leader, she was the lead singer and drummer, and like her musical hero, Karen Carpenter, placed her drum set in the front of the other instrumentalists, leading the worship band, in the second service, with the wave of her drumsticks.

Diane began. "On Sunday some of us got some pushback on the survey we took. One old dude asked me why we needed all that information. He said, 'Jesus never took a survey. He looked to his Father in heaven and just did what his Father told him to.' Then I thought, well, did Jesus ever take an assessment? Did he ever take a survey? Did Jesus ask any questions? And here's what I found. In the gospels, Jesus asked 307 questions and answered only three of them himself. I think Jesus asked questions in order to find out more about the person he was ministering to. That person's answer would influence what Jesus should do next."

Tom smiled with satisfaction. Diana was thinking the same thing he was. It was that thinking that got him out of his pickle with Harold and the elders.

"So, what are some of the questions that come to mind?" asked Diana. There was a brief silence then the answers started coming. Diana wrote the questions on the white board.

"What do you want me to do for you?" answered Libby.

"Do you believe I can do this?" answered Tanika.

"What is your name?" answered Elliott.

"Woman, where are your accusers? Has no one condemned you?" answered Kaiya.

"Who do you say that I am?" answered Jerome.

"Why were you looking for me?" answered Juan.

"Do you have any fish?" answered Dan.

"Do you want to get well?" answered Diana.

"Do you love me?" answered Lonnie.

"That's plenty. But you get the picture. Okay, pair up with another person," instructed Diana. Diana quickly assigned a verse to each pair of staff along with two questions to answer, "What did Jesus do with the information he learned?" "And what might he have done if the answer to his question had been different?"

The discussion was robust. Diana regained control of the room and landed the plane. "If Jesus didn't guess what people wanted or needed, I think that's why this survey we took is so timely. Our questions set us up for what we should do next and I'm really looking forward to what we learn."

"That was super, Diana," said Tom. "Very well-done staff. It's all about knowing more about the person in front of us so we can match them to what God has for them." Tom was excited to introduce the team to his latest discovery. "This morning I want to introduce you to something called, 'The Net Promoter Score' or the "NPS." Tom went through a bit of the history of the NPS from an article in *Harvard Business Review* called 'The One

Number You Need to Grow" from the December 2003 issue. One quote stood out, which he read to the team from his iPhone.

> "It turned out that a single survey question can, in fact, serve as a useful predictor of growth. But that question isn't about customer satisfaction or even loyalty—at least in so many words. Rather, it's about a customers' willingness to recommend a product or service to someone else. In fact, in most of the industries that I studied, the percentage of customers who were enthusiastic enough to refer a friend or colleague—perhaps the strongest sign of customer loyalty—correlated directly with differences in growth rates among competitors... This number is the one number you need to grow. It's that simple and that profound."

Tom continued. "So, if you remember, we included the NPS question on the survey we took a couple weeks ago." Tom passed out the hundred completed surveys and asked the staff to divide them into three piles—the Detractors (0s-6s), the Passives (7s and 8s) and the Promoters (9s & 10s) and then count them. There were thirty-three Detractors, thirty-nine Promoters and twenty-eight Passives. So, in his head Tom subtracted the percentage of Detractors from the percentage of Promoters and got a shockingly low score of six. Six?!?!? What's up with that? I've got to talk to Bob, he demanded in his mind. Tom remained calm and continued with his instructions for the next exercise. "OK, for now set aside the twenty-eight Passives and divide into two groups. Now each group gets a stack of half the Promoters and Half the Detractors." Once both stacks had been divided Tom continued, "Here's what you want to look for; correlations within the 9s and 10s and 0s through 6s and then any correlations or contrasts between the two groups so you might want to start with looking at what do the 9s and 10s do that the 0-6s are not doing? Correlation is about finding the connections. So, find out any connections between the NPS and their age, frequency of attendance, small group involvement, service, etc."

The two groups eagerly dove into their task at hand. Tom sat back and watched the action and listened to the bustling conversations.

"It looks like the more frequently people attend, the higher their NPS. Anybody else seeing that?"

"Look at the difference in the scores between people who have a good friend at church and those who don't."

"Are you guys seeing how many people decided to stay because one of the pastors invited them to come back the following week?"

"I haven't found anyone yet that has had a spiritual conversation with...oh wait...here's one."

"All of my promoters so far are also givers. Oh no...here's one who doesn't give but he's only been attending for two months."

Fourteen Fridays - 77

While the two teams worked feverishly recording their observations on sticky notes, Tom stepped up to the large whiteboard and with a black erasable marker drew five large vertical boxes. He then labeled these boxes,

ATTRACT　　　GET　　　KEEP　　　GROW　　　MULTIPLY

And then Tom sat down. The conversation was electric and within forty-five minutes both teams had finished their assignment, eagerly waiting for what would come next. Tom gave a brief definition of each of the five movements of the Church Engagement Framework and concluded by saying, "What we want to solve for is how we might attract more people, get more people into an event or service, keep more people, grow more people and multiply more people who are multiplying our mission." One person after another enthusiastically explained their discovery and placed their sticky note in the appropriate box on the white board.

"We found that the people in both groups who have attended here for the shortest amount of time were the most likely to have had spiritual conversations with non-Christians."

"When we looked at the 0s through 6s none of them were doing more than one of our growth activities. So, they might be in a small group but don't serve or give."

"I see that most folks who are on a growth journey also have a trusted friend here."

"We saw that the longer people attended, if they were not on a growth journey, they were the least likely to recommend Daybreak Church to their friends and colleagues."

And for the next 15 minutes every one of the staff got out of their chair and posted at least two or three significant observations. The room still buzzed with the energy of fresh discovery as Tom got out of his chair. "So, here's what we did. We started looking at demographic and behavioral data and then we kept adding more data until we could see a correlation or connection between two things...say spiritual growth and having a friend at church. That's what correlation does. But that doesn't mean that correlation equals causation. Then Tom referred to an illustration Bob told him on Friday evening somewhere in the eighth inning. "Just because the per capita consumption of mozzarella cheese near perfectly corresponds to the number of doctorates awarded in Civil Engineering doesn't mean that one caused the other. 'Insight' is our big 'aha' where we discover a possible cause and effect relationship." Tom stepped up to another white board and sketched out the first half of the Insight Engine. "'Data—Analytics—Insight.' That's how far we've gotten this morning. So, if we think that there is more than a correlation...that there might be a causation, we form a hypothesis and then we run an experiment to test our hypothesis and the results give us an answer in the form of new data which allows us to start this cycle over and over again," Tom said, retracing the figure-eight of the Insight Engine. "So, here's where I'd like to take this. I'd like to form five teams of three people each based on the Church Engagement Framework. I'm going to be part of the Multiply team because...well...just because I called it first," Tom smiled. "Each movement in the Church Engagement Framework is critical to the future of the church so just go write your name on the group you want to be part of. If there are already three names in that box, please choose another area to work on."

The staff got out of their seats and did as they were instructed and Tom continued, "So now get in your different teams and starting with the data and analysis, create a hypothesis on what you think would attract more people, get more people, keep more people, grow more and better disciples and multiply those who are multiplying the mission of the church. Then each team needs to create an experiment to test their hypothesis. I've got Chipotle coming in about an hour so let's get right to work. At the end of the hour each team will report out on three things—what they saw in the data, the hypothesis they came up with and one experiment their team will run over the next six weeks."

"Remind us again what a hypothesis is? It's been a while since I had a science class," asked James, the Communications Coordinator.

"Oh, uh, right," said Tom. It's just one sentence and it goes something like this... 'We believe that if we do _____, it will lead to more of / less of _____.' So, grab one of these big sticky posters and some markers and get to it. Got it? See you back here around 12:15."

Two teams continued their work in the conference room while the other teams found their ideal working environments in other parts of the building.

Sixty minutes passed too quickly so when Tom rounded up the teams, most were scrambling to complete their assignment. "OK before we eat, I just want each team to put your poster paper on the wall and simply read what you've written regarding what you saw in the data, what's your hypothesis for change and the experiment you will run to prove or disprove your hypothesis over the next six weeks. Let's start with 'Attract' and my team will finish up with 'Multiply.'"

Stephanie, the Director of Community Ministry began. "OK, here's what we came up with. We saw in the data that over thirty percent of the people who have been attending for less than a year, heard about our church for the first time because of something they saw on social media—mostly on Facebook for that Go Fund Me campaign we did to raise money for the iPad tablets for Denver Public Schools. Our hypothesis is, "We believe that the more we let our light shine through the good we are doing in the community, the more Daybreak people will post about it on Facebook and Instagram and that will cause more people to be aware that we exist in the community. Our experiment is to ask the people of Daybreak to create at least one Facebook or Instagram post on the food drive we are doing in two weeks, then measure to see if we have an uptick of 'Likes' on Facebook and more traffic on our Website."

"Great work," said Tom with pride. "You nailed it—great hypothesis and experiment. OK, who's presenting for Get? Is that you James?"

James, the Communications Coordinator enthusiastically began. "In the data, we saw that 90 percent of people, in all age groups came to Daybreak for the first time because someone in the church invited them and only ten percent of our people invited someone in the past six months. Our hypothesis is that if we created a small business card for each new sermon series, that explained what people would learn and experience in that series, that our people would be more willing and more able to invite their colleagues to Daybreak Church and we'd double the amount of Daybreak Church people who invite others. So, our experiment is to create one business card based on Tom's series in Nehemiah. 'Rebuilding Hope' with a weblink to our two-minute video intro to the series, like we did for Pastor Tom's series on sex...what was it? Oh yeah, 'The heaving bosom of Abraham.' We'll explain the purpose of the cards in Sunday's services and make the cards available in the sanctuary and the Fellowship Hall."

"Really good work. OK...who is presenting for 'Keep?'"

Kaiya, the Middle School Director, confidently walked up to the poster labeled "KEEP" and began. "I want to say a few things about 'Get' that relate to 'Keep.' From the data we see that people who visit Daybreak Church for the first time have actually watched us online at least three times before their first live visit. It's like our website is part of their spiritual Tinder app where people can check a church out and then swipe right or swipe left." Now that Kaiya had their attention, she continued. "Those folks who do actually walk in the door for the first time are checking us out like they are on a first date. They want to see if the reality matches up with the profile picture so to speak. In dating it is the second date, not the first date where people decide if the relationship is worth pursuing. It's where a guy's plain looks are enhanced by how clever or kind he is..."

"Or how rich he is!" laughed Jerome. The staff chuckled.

Kaiya had played Volleyball at Puget Sound University, so noise from the stands only emboldened her and she soldiered on. "We on the Keep team are all single and all about getting that second and third date." The staff smiled and a few nodded.

"So, what's your hypothesis and experiment Kai?" asked Tom.

"Well, the research shows that 60 percent of visitors who attend a church three times make that church their home church. Our hypothesis, which comes from the dating experience, is that the best time to ask for a second date is at the end of the first date. So, we believe that if we ask every first-time visitor to visit three weeks in a row, from the stage, that we will experience an increase in new visitor retention. Our experiment is to end every service with an invitation for guests to attend the next two consecutive services and see what happens."

"Very clever Kai," said Tom. "How about Grow...Uh...take it Jerome."

"This was so interesting for us. We took a look at the data that showed what the Net Promoters did in their growth journey that the Net Detractors did not do. Here's our biggest 'aha!' from the data. All of our Net Promoters were satisfied with their spiritual growth and health. And we noticed that all of them are involved in a small group. By contrast nearly all of our Net Detractors were not satisfied with their level of growth and health. Seems it doesn't matter how many times they come to church, if they are merely attending, they are not growing. Seems that being on a growth journey with other believers increases not only spiritual satisfaction but increases the willingness to invite someone to Daybreak. It's a double win."

Tom smiled. "That's a great insight Jerome. So, what's your hypothesis and experiment?"

Jerome began. "Here is our hypothesis: We believe that people are more likely to be satisfied with their spiritual progress and will more likely be promoters of Daybreak Church if they are part of a small group. To validate our hypothesis each of us on the team is going to start a four-week small group made up of people who have never been part of a small group before. We'll personally invite five people in our sphere of influence and invite them to be part of this four-week group. Before the group begins, we'll take a two-question assessment around NPS and their level of satisfaction. Then after the four weeks do the same to see if involvement in a small group makes the difference."

"Sounds like a great experiment Jerome. Can't wait to see what you discover. Well, I guess it's time for 'Multiply.' I'll be short since our lunch has arrived. So, here's what we saw in the data. About 40 percent of our people are contributing to fulfilling the mission of Daybreak Church through giving over $500 a year, leading a small group or church ministry, serving through one of our ministries, inside or outside the church, inviting their neighbors, evangelizing or discipling someone. Sixty percent are still just consumers of our mission. So, our goal in 'Multiply' is about moving people from consumers of the mission to actual contributors to the mission. Oh, and we found some data in the Bible that helps shape our hypothesis and experiment. Renee pointed out that people came to Jesus 'to hear his words and be healed of their diseases.' They were just consumers. But Jesus' purpose was to 'seek and to save...to serve and to give' and that's the change he wants for all his followers." Tom felt he was starting to preach so finished up. "Our hypothesis is that over time, people are more satisfied through what they contribute than what they consume, the more people we help get on mission the healthier they and we, as a church, will be. So, our experiment is to create weekly opportunities to say 'yes' to one of these contributor activities at the end of my sermons. We'll create some type of tool to measure their progress."

Tom was through but sensed he was just beginning. He was Michelangelo placing his chisel against the marble block from which David would emerge. There was no turning back. "I just want to say how impressed I am with all of your creative ideas. Let's eat! Who wants to thank the Lord for the food and for the morning we've had?"

Tom's Executive Pastor, Dan, stepped alongside Tom at the back of the food line. "This is the best staff meeting I've ever been a part of. Very well done." Tom felt his spirits rise.

"Thanks Dan. That means a lot."

At the elder meeting
The elder meeting came all too soon, but Tom was energized by the morning's staff meeting and was eager to share the experiments the staff would be running. At 6:55 Tom was busy welcoming the elders as they grabbed their cups of decaf and a Rice Krispy Treat. At 7pm Harold called the meeting to order. Tom was glad that he had started delegating devotionals. People are more fulfilled by contribution than consumption, he reminded himself. Elder Burnie Dye was the funeral director of Dye Funeral Home—a business founded by his grandfather in 1927. Although the church constitution required that elder board members rotate off for one year, every six years, for all intents and purposes, Burnie, like the other elders had been on the elder board for over twenty-five years. Impeccably dressed and perfectly coiffed, even on his days off, Burnie opened the Scriptures to Jeremiah 6 and read from the King James Version.

"'Thus, saith the Lord, 'Stand ye in the ways, and see, and ask for the old paths, where is the good way, and walk therein, and ye shall find rest for your souls.' But they said, 'We will not walk therein.'"

Now in his early 70s this passage was Burnie's go-to passage. There was something about the good way being found in the old paths for his church...and his business. Over the past couple of decades as cremation replaced burial as the preferred way to be interred, Burnie was seeing his margins decrease and his once thriving business was now on life support. "The only cremation in the Bible was Achan...and he was no saint. Christians are to be buried or how will God resurrect them?" Burnie would often repeat. Little wonder he longed for the good old days. But the verse about asking for the old paths hit a nerve with the elders that set the tone for the evening and reminiscing about the church's glory days was enough to spark a vigorous conversation on the way forward for Daybreak Church. Seeking the ancient ways and asking God for the old paths seemed like the scripturally sound thing to do. The minutes from the April elder meeting were read and approved and Harold asked Tom to give a report on the survey they had taken nine days earlier. Tom was ready with a short PowerPoint presentation that showed the results of the Net Promoter survey and was about to report out on the experiments the staff were running but it was too late. The dye had been cast. Jeremiah 6 and the returning to the old paths was the anchor-point of the discussion and little progress could be made that night.

It was a hard night for Tom. His prayer life was questioned. It was suggested that he was trying to make data the fourth member of the Trinity. One old saint insinuated that Tom was more enamored with Peter Drucker than Peter the Apostle. The discussion ended with Harold addressing Tom as "Brother." That was a Christian practice that Tom despised. Calling someone 'Brother' implied you could say anything you wanted to say, no matter how hurtful, because it was couched in a familial manner. "Brother," Harold said.

'We want the best for you and we want what's best for Daybreak Church. But we need a pastor to lead us, not a data scientist to confuse us. I think I speak for the elder board when I say that the way forward is found in the Scriptures, not in a survey. And you've got four months to figure that out."

It was a gut punch Tom was not expecting and Tom remembered little of what was discussed after that. Something about the Women's Brunch, the location of the Fall Men's retreat...just spiritual dribble. What the heck am I doing here, he thought.

At home

It was a little after nine when Tom sullenly entered his home. Amy was up emptying the dishwasher. "Sometimes I think I'm a glutton for punishment," said Tom. "I don't know why I ever wanted to be a pastor. Sometimes I think I must be delusional to think that I can change the church."

'Sounds like the elder meeting didn't go well," sympathized Amy.

"That'd be an understatement," said Tom. "I didn't even have the opportunity to explain some of the new things we were trying. And in some ways, I'm glad I didn't because I think the elders would have shut them down. At least for now we can try to move forward."

"That bad huh? I'm sorry Honey. Let me fix you a little something and you can tell me all about those bozos you have to report to," said Amy with a sympathetic smile. And Amy's candidness and humor lifted Tom's spirits. Life wasn't over for him yet.

May 31. Colorado Rockies v. Toronto Blue Jays

It was the last day in May and the Toronto Blue Jays were in town. It was a warm, late Denver afternoon and Tom put his Astros baseball cap on his head for the short stride to Coors field. Summer had arrived. This was becoming a comfortable routine, enjoying the buoyant effect of seeing families and friends walking together towards the stadium, grabbing his burrito and a couple bags of peanuts outside the stadium. But this evening was different. He was still reeling and feeling a bit unsteady from his time with Harold and the elders.

Rockies' German Márquez was just finishing warming up when Tom tossed a bag of peanuts to Bob and took his seat on the aisle. After an exchange of cordiality, Bob looked at Tom. "You look like crap, Tom. You feel O.K.?"

"I look that bad huh?" Tom said, trying to force a grin. "It was actually a good week. We set up a bunch of hypotheses and experiments around the Church Engagement Framework on Tuesday morning but then we had the elder's meeting Tuesday night. It was so discouraging I hardly had the opportunity to tell the elders all we were doing. I felt like a lamb before the slaughter. It was just awful."

"Well, tell me about your hypotheses and experiments," said Bob. "Maybe I'll be a better sounding board than your elder board. What did you all figure out with your net promoter stuff?"

Tom had been so wound up about the elder meeting that the urgency of telling Bob about all the experiments had moved from the front to the back burner. "Oh, it went really well," said Tom. "Because of all the other questions we were able to find patterns about what people with high NPS scores did that those with low NPS scores didn't do."

"Any big surprises?" asked Bob.

"The first correlation that we noticed was about attendance being correlated to NPS scores. Our highest NPS scores were by those who attended four times a month," said Tom. We also saw that attending alone did not produce Net Promoters. The Net Promoters were all involved in at least one other growth activity like serving in the community or being in a small group," said Tom. "Really interesting stuff. So, show me your T-shirt Bob."

Bob turned toward Tom.

THE GOAL IS TO TURN DATA INTO INSIGHT AND INSIGHT INTO ACTION

"I can't emphasize that enough. Without action, data is a party trick. So, how did you turn interesting into actionable?" asked Bob. He was not going to let Tom off the hook.

"We're on it, Bob. I broke our staff into five teams around Attract, Get, Keep, Grow and Multiply and let the staff choose what area they had the most passion for," said Tom. Tom then went through the data, hypotheses and experiments each team was going to over the next six weeks. "Oh, here's a card the communications group came up with telling you about my sermon series on Nehemiah along with a link to see what it might be like to attend Daybreak Church," Tom said. Wow, Tom thought. He had just personally invited someone to come to church. That hadn't happened since he moved to Denver.

"That is really good Tom and I have to say how impressed I am," said Bob. "I'd love to hear the results when they come in. And don't let those elders define who you are."

"Of course," said Tom, smiling. It felt good to be acknowledged and appreciated.

The Rockies started off strong with a crushing 469 feet, two-run home run by Trevor Story early in the bottom of the first inning. By the bottom of the third inning the Rockies had increased their lead to 10-2. May had been a good month for the Rockies and they came into the game with a 29-27 win-loss record. They had won five games straight and it looked like number six was on the way. The lead lifted Tom's spirits and also created margin for a deeper conversation. "There's something I've been meaning to ask you Bob," said Tom.

"What's that?" asked Bob.

"How is it that you know so much dang Scripture?" asked Tom. "I mean you're like the good version of elder Harold."

"Hah!" said Bob. "Thanks a lot. I haven't told you my story? Huh! I think I was in church probably every Sunday since I was born really with my dad being a pastor and all. The Bible was really important in his ministry. Especially in the early years. He had a good mind for memorizing, so he memorized a lot of Scripture, chapters and even books of the New Testament. Because that was his value, it was just something I thought that kids did with their dads. So, by the time I got out of high school I had a pretty good grasp of the Bible, but it never seemed to change me in the dramatic ways it changed some of my friends who came from more secular homes. After graduating high school, I went to UCLA and was one of the leaders of a big student ministry there and was directing the high school ministry at my dad's church. I went to lots of conferences and summer projects, did a lot of ministry and entertained the idea of following in my dad's footsteps. But when I graduated in 1998 a fraternity brother asked me to help start a technology company. The internet was only four years old and there was a lot of upside for tech. He had this vision for helping companies with data and analytics and needed someone in sales, which suited me fine. It was a grind but eventually the market caught up with what we provided especially after we figured out the culture of our company. As I began to learn about data and analytics, I began to see it everywhere in the Bible. With my Christian clients and the megachurches we worked with I got pretty good at connecting data and dogma. Then I met Dana and got married in 2008 and then moved out here a couple years ago. I just haven't been all that involved in actual church for quite a while. But I suppose that's OK."

"You were single a long time," commented Tom.

"Yeah, sometimes it takes a while to find the right one," said Bob. "But I've found the right one."

"Me too," said Tom.

The Rockies had a big night. German Márquez pitched seven innings, striking out seven batters and allowing a stingy four hits. Márquez also had a big night at the plate, batting two-for-three before yielding to his relief pitcher. Before the night ended, Trevor Story hit another walloping home run and had seven RBIs to show for his night's work.

"See you next week at the Padres game?" asked Tom.

"Wouldn't miss it," said Bob. "One of these nights I should bring Dana and you can bring Amy and we can go to dinner beforehand or maybe drinks afterwards."

"That might be nice. Let's get something on the calendar," said Tom.

Walking home, Tom felt a burden lifted. I guess relationships do catalyze growth, he found himself thinking. Bob's sure a catalyst to my growth.

At home

"Amy, I'm home," said Tom as he walked through the door.

"Oh good. I was just about to watch *The Crown* and was hoping you could join me. It's really getting good."

Tom hesitated. He was beat after such a stressful week, but it had been a week since Amy and he had any time alone. "Yeah, that sounds great. I'll make some popcorn. What do you want to drink?"

Chapter eight

At church

Pastors like to say that Sundays come along with alarming frequency and soon Tom was standing behind the lectern, teaching from Nehemiah 6. If the truth be told, most pastors can't remember what they spoke on last weekend. It's the brain's way of creating space for this week's sermon preparation. But Nehemiah 6 was personally impactful for Tom. Nehemiah 6 recounted Nehemiah's progress on rebuilding the wall along with the growing opposition of his arch enemies Sanballat and Tobiah who had recruited a number of Jewish people to oppose what Nehemiah was attempting. It was a familiar pattern. Whenever God wants something important done there will be opposition and maybe the bigger the task...the greater the opposition. Harold had recruited the elders who were determined to get rid of Tom.

A highlight of the service was watching Stephanie, the Director of Community Engagement, give the announcement about Daybreak's food drive she was kicking off. "The most repeated words of Jesus are said every morning around the world...even by people who don't yet know him." She had everyone's attention now. "Jesus' words are recorded in John 21:12 where he says, 'Come and have breakfast.' Through our food drive, we are going to help the children of Denver accept Jesus' invitation to breakfast and perhaps this will lead them to accepting Jesus' other invitations to follow him and make him Lord of their lives." Both services broke out in applause.

At church in the all-hands staff meeting

Monday's all-hands meeting lifted Tom's spirits even more. Dan, the Executive Pastor, led off with an insightful devotional. Dan was a retired engineer and project manager from IBM and was well-fitted to sit in the second chair. At 66 he still had a lot of fire in his belly and was excited to see the church's new interest in data.

Dan began. "My one hobby is fishing. Lately I've been learning to fly fish, but any kind of fishing is good for me. The notorious bank robber, Willy Sutton, was once asked why he robbed banks. His answer? 'Because that's where the money is.' The staff chuckled looking forward to his point. "So, I fish in the water because that's where the fish are, but I rarely know specifically in the water where I can find them. So, this week I went to the Scriptures to see what I could learn, and I looked at the fisherman Peter and his fishing encounters with Jesus."

The staff leaned in toward Dan curious to see how he would continue. "Early in his ministry Jesus asked Peter if he had caught any fish. No, he'd been skunked. So, Jesus said, 'Why don't you row out into the deep water and put your net down.' Peter reluctantly followed Jesus' suggestion and ended up with two boatloads of fish. After Jesus' resurrection, Jesus encounters the fishless Peter in his boat and suggests that Peter cast his net on the right side of the boat. Peter obeys and pulls in 153 fish. The third time Jesus talked with Peter about fishing was when Peter asked him about whether they should pay taxes to Caesar. This time Jesus' answer was to take a line and hook and throw it into the lake and the first fish he pulled up would have a coin in its mouth—enough to pay the tax bill of Peter and Jesus." The staff nodded in approval but were still waiting for the punchline. "Here's the point. Peter wanted to catch fish, he was an expert fisherman, his livelihood depended on catching fish. He just didn't know where the fish were. I believe every day in Denver there are people who want to take their next step with Jesus. We just don't know who they are. But that's where data comes in. Data can tell us with great accuracy who wants to get closer to God and the best way to communicate with that person. Think of Peter's variables. Shallow water, deep water...left side of the boat, right side of the boat...day fishing, night fishing...using a net or using a hook. Oh, there's one more thing Jesus said about fishing. He said to Peter, 'Follow me and I will make you a fisher of men. And just like I showed you where the hungry fish were, I'll show you where the people who hunger for me are.' I think technology and data analytics is God's gift to the church to show us where the hungry people are and I'm personally excited about where we are going with this initiative." The staff nodded in agreement. This was all so new to them, but it was also exciting to be on the brink of discovery.

"That was excellent, Dan," said Tom. The rest of the all-hands was taken up reviewing the progress each team was making to prove or disprove their hypotheses.

When Tom got home, at the end of the day, Amy gave Tom a casual greeting and Tom realized how preoccupied he'd been with the church. What does it profit a man to gain his church but lose his wife, he pondered?

"What do you think about grabbing a little dinner together?" asked Tom.

Amy smiled. "I'd love to."

Friday, June 14. Colorado Rockies v. San Diego Padres
The San Diego Padres were in town. With the ending of the first inning, the usher at the top of the stairs released the waiting fans to find their seats. As Tom was finishing his burrito, he heard a friendly voice. "Hey Tom."

Tom looked up, and then smiling said, "Glad you can make it."

"Yeah, sorry I'm late. I had to drive in from the Springs. Had an all-day consultation with a start-up company called PrayerChimp and the traffic was stop-and-go from Monument Hill to the Tech Center. Must've been some kind of accident."

"PrayerChimp? What kind of company is that?" asked Tom.

"It's a great concept. Their tagline is something like, 'PrayerChimp: For people who believe in the power of prayer but are too busy to pray themselves.'"

"Yeah, I get that. So how does it work?" asked Tom.

"Pretty simple really. PrayerChimp is a platform that connects people who need prayer with women who are really good at praying. So, on the supply side, PrayerChimp works with anti-trafficking organizations that rescue girls and places them into recovery and care homes. These young women begin by just praying all types of Scripture and blessings, even if they themselves are not believers. Then on the demand side, I get a notification of what has been prayed on my behalf that day." Bob reached for his phone. "So, this morning I got a notification that said, 'Here's what we prayed for you today from Psalm 23.

'Dear Bob,
May the Lord be your Shepherd today.
May you not be in want.
May you find rest and your soul be restored today.
If you go through the Valley of the Shadow of Death, may God hold your hand.
If you are at the table with your enemies, may God protect you and give you wisdom.
And know today that God has a place for you in heaven.
In the name of Jesus, Amen'

Bob gathered his composure and continued. "So, every day I get a notification like that. It really makes my day to know that a team of women has been interceding for me. And that's just the basic offering of $30 a month and $30 a month can go a long way in Nepal. So, they've also found that just praying Scripture every day on behalf of someone else leads to a spiritual conversion of the ones who intercede. It's quite amazing but over 95 percent of these women become Christians in this process. They become new creatures in Christ. They have a new identity in Christ. Soon they are in some type of vocational training and are thriving on their own. Contrast that to other efforts to rescue and restore. Typically, half of the rescued women return to the sex trade because of the shame and guilt. With PrayerChimp these women are restored and made new. They feel powerful because they can change outcomes through intercession. I'm a big fan of PrayerChimp."

"So, it's not actually chimps who are praying for you?" asked Tom with a smile. "It's more of a service like MailChimp but it is the women who are the intercessors."

"That's right. And they have other levels of prayer. So, for $80 a month, they have access to my Google Calendar. So, if I were about to go into an important client meeting, I might get a notification that said the PrayerChimp team was praying for my success. So, like any good platform, it creates a win for both sides."

"Fascinating," said Tom. "So, what do you do during an all-day consultation?"

"Well, if I told you how simple it is, I'd have to kill you," Bob smiled but could tell Tom was anxious to learn more. "PrayerChimp has around forty employees, has raised a decent amount of capital but is plateaued in their sales. Over the years we've found that the problem we are asked to solve is rarely the real problem. So, to figure out what was happening in the company we sent out an extensive assessment to every employee from the CEO to the part-time intern and asked each one to answer around a hundred and twenty questions about the company."

"What kind of questions?" asked Tom.

"They are pretty specific questions around the company's mission, strategy...company values and culture, leadership, compensation, business model, recognition and rewards, theory of change, innovation...that kind of stuff. And we ask that all employees to be very specific using a four-point scale where the meaning of each number is clearly defined," Bob explained.

"What do you mean?" asked Tom. "'Where each number is clearly defined?'"

"Take the question about the vision of the company. The question might be something like, 'How powerful is our vision as a magnet that pulls us into the future?' '1' would be defined as *'I'm not sure we have a company vision. If we do, I haven't seen it.'* '2' might be something like *'We have a vision statement on the wall, but it is rarely referred to.'* '3' might be *'We have a clear and compelling vision that many have bought into and is often used to set priorities and direction.'* And '4' will be something *like 'We have a clear, specific and inspiring vision that is embraced by all employees and consistently used to set direction and actions.'* Being really specific eliminates a lot of subjectivity. And every person is able to submit written comments along with their numerical score if they want to make any suggestions for improvement."

"So, what happens next?" asked Tom.

"All this is anonymous and is done online so when the surveys are completed, we get back two reports. The first report is three or four pages that reports on all 120 questions and indicates two things—the average score and the degree of consensus on the score. So high average scores and high consensus scores are color-coded in a different color than medium and low scores. The second report, which only our team and the C-level people see is around 20 pages or so that shows the results along with participant comments.

"So, how'd it go today when you went over the results?" asked Tom.

"Well, we started off by going around the room and asking people to introduce themselves, what role they played and how long they'd been with the company. Then we went over a few ground rules that are pretty important to the process. We then broke them into eight groups of five—which is the optimal number for decision making and gave them a poster-size template laid out something like this." Bob pulled a 3x5 card out of his back pocket and wrote,

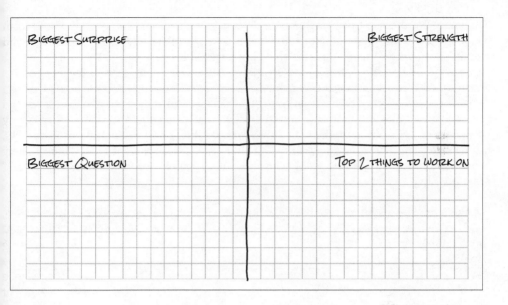

BIGGEST SURPRISE

BIGGEST STRENGTH

BIGGEST QUESTION

TOP 2 THINGS TO WORK ON

Then each team took 50 minutes to fill out their template based on the data. Our only stipulation was their answers needed to be grounded in the data from the survey, which makes it difficult to hijack the agenda. When someone made an observation or proposal, the fair question to ask is 'Where do you see this in the data?' My T-shirt was a good visual reminder."

Bob handed the 3x5 card to Tom as he slowly Tom read aloud, the white letters on Bob's black T-shirt.

WHERE DO YOU SEE THAT IN THE DATA?

"Wow, sounds like a good day," said Tom, imagining how he might use such a process. He wanted to know more but also realized Bob may actually want to watch the game rather than talk business. He tested the waters. "So, what happened next?"

Bob kept his eye on the field but answered. "Oh yeah, so one at a time each team took three minutes to explain their template. My partner, who is a great facilitator, would always ask, 'where do you see that in the data?' After each of the eight teams presented, we had a short debrief and then had lunch—a bunch of subs and salads from Subway."

The Padres struck first and held onto a 1-0 lead going into the bottom of the third inning.

"So, what happened after lunch?" asked Tom.

"Oh, yeah. We did a bit of review on the morning session and introduced the idea of hypotheses and experimentation. On a white board we listed the eight things that the individual teams had come up with that they wanted to work on that would make the biggest difference in the future of the company. There were quite a few duplicates, so we ended up with just five things to work on. Then we passed out markers so each person could vote for their top three most important areas by placing hash-marks next to the topic they thought was most important to the future of the company. So, after five minutes we had identified...based on the data...the top three things they wanted to work on—the three biggest problems they needed to solve that would take them into the future. Then, we created three groups and people chose which problem they wanted to work on and contribute to.

We had a final template for the three groups to fill out. It looked something like this...Oh, here I took a picture of it." Bob pinched his fingers to zoom out on the template and showed the photo to Tom.

Team:		Date: __/__/____
What problem are you solving for?	Hypothesis #1: "We believe if we do _____ _____ _____ the result will be _____ _____ (our desired outcome)"	Experiment #1 What you will do: Who will lead it? How you will measure it?
What would an "Epic Win" look like in six months?		

"So, after an hour each team presented their plan followed by genuine appreciative applause. They now have a plan to take them forward. We finished up with a time of sharing what the day meant to each participant. 'Energizing,' 'Best meeting ever,' 'Can we do this every week?' Things like that. There were even some tears. Probably the most common word was 'hope.' But other expressions were about feeling so valued for the first time in a long time. There was so much energy still in the room at the end of the day. Many of them had experienced what it was like to be part of a true learning team for the first time."

"What do you mean, 'learning team?'" asked Tom.

"Well, a true learning team is one where the least qualified person can make the greatest contribution because ideas and contributions are weighed against the mission or against the problem they are solving, rather than against the position or tenure of the contributor. So, one of the guys who made some of the greatest contributions was Toby, the facilities manager. He had never been asked to come to any meeting before and coming from Haiti...well it was a pretty sweet moment."

"Sounds like an amazing day but it looks like they did all the work. I pictured consulting work as giving principles and advice," said Tom.

"And that's why I have to kill you now," said Bob coldly. "You now know the secret. Well, I guess if I can't kill you I can still buy you a cold one."

"Deal!" said Tom and the two friends headed upstairs to the concession stand.

"So how will you follow up with the PrayerChimp team?" asked Tom, once they were settled in their seats.

"Well, like all organizations, PrayerChimp needs to get more proficient creating hypotheses and running experiments so I'll get on a Zoom call with them every six weeks for the next six-months to help them interpret the data they get from their first experiment and help them formulate additional experiments till they achieve their epic win."

What do you mean, 'epic win?'" asked Tom.

"I first heard the concept from the game designer, Jane McGonigal, at a convention in San Francisco a few years ago. I liked her definition so much that I pretty much memorized it. She said an epic win is an outcome that is so extraordinarily positive you had no idea it was even possible until you achieved it. So, an epic win would be Brandi Chastain in the 1999 world cup, or Rulon Gardner upsetting the undefeated Aleksandr Karelin in the Sydney Olympic Greco Roman wrestling finals. It's Tiger sinking that final putt in the 2005 Masters. It's Doug Flutie after throwing that amazing pass with no time left to beat Miami. And an epic win is always expressed the same way anywhere in the world." With that Bob raised both arms over his head and clenched his fist. "The Italians even have a word for that emotion and expression—'*Fiero*!" It's the feeling you get when you win so big that it even surprises you."

"*Fiero*!" Tom said.

"Do you have anything in your life that would be an epic win Tom?" asked Bob. What would be a win so big in your life that it would surprise even you?"

"Got to think about that one," said Tom. Tom thought for a moment. What would an epic win look like in my life...with Amy...with the church...in my golf game? I've got to give some thought to that.

The sixth inning was huge for the Rockies. Ian Desmond hit a rare inside the park home run. "That only occurs one of 158 home runs," offered Bob. "I don't know why I remember numbers like that, but I do." The Rockies batted through the order and by the time their side was retired they were in a commanding lead 9-3 and an inning later the Rockies were leading 11-4. This game was over and thousands of fans confidently headed for the exits.

"So, what's the odds of the visiting team coming back from a 7-run deficit at the top of the eighth inning?" asked Tom.

Bob reached into his pocket. "Let me see. It's only happened twice in 2,713 games that have been played since 1957 where the home team was ahead by seven going into the eighth. So, it is basically a 100 percent chance of victory. San Diego is screwed. We got this one in the bag. If you were a betting man, it's safe to say you can bet the farm on the outcome of this game Tom," said Bob.

"It's funny," said Tom. "I've been thinking how to describe my emotions this week and what you just said about the Padres resonated with me. I'm screwed. I'll be finished in September. Sure, God could do it but I'm just not sure what I'd do if I weren't a pastor."

"I'm sorry," said Bob. "That was insensitive of me. If the last call for beer hadn't been given, I'd buy you a beer. How about some cotton candy or some Cracker Jacks?" Tom couldn't help but smile.

At the top of the eighth inning the Padres Hunter Renfro stepped up to the plate. An unseasonable warm whisper of air, a wind of possibility...a lucky wind, swept through Coors field as Renfro hit a bouncing ball that hit shortstop Trevor Story in the face. Renfro was safely on first base. Story always got his man on first but now was taken out of the game and the Rockies repositioned their infield players.

"Before we split, there's something I wanted to talk to you about. You know, the difference between involvement and engagement. I think I understand but I want to be able to explain it better." said Tom.

"Well, when we talked about Attract, Get, Keep, Grow and Multiply we said that those in the Multiply stage were those who were *multiplying* the mission of the church. We called them "engaged" because they were engaged in fulfilling the mission of the church, they weren't just consumers of what the church had to offer. It's really quite binary whether people are consuming or contributing. And the research shows that it is the engaged believers that make the biggest difference."

"What do you mean by 'research?'" asked Tom.

"The Gallop research organization has done a lot of work on the topic of engagement. Thirty-some years ago they started studying what it means for employees to be engaged in their jobs. They surveyed over 30 million employees, so the data is quite robust. About ten years ago they started studying church engagement and discovered that, similar to workplaces, something like only 29 percent of church people are engaged but this 29 percent has a disproportionate impact on the church. They are the keystone species of every church. Let me look it up…. OK, here it is…'Engaged congregants are more than ten times as likely to invite someone to participate in their congregations, nearly three times as likely to say they are extremely satisfied with their lives…spend more than two hours each week serving and helping others in their community and three times more likely to give to their faith communities.'"

"That's good stuff," Tom said. The Padres Austin Hedges hit a double to deep left field driving in Renfro. Rockies 11, Padres 5.

"This game's over. It's my anniversary this weekend, so we have big plans. We're spending the weekend at the Broadmoor down in the Springs. We got the Honeymoon package for Saturday night. It'll be eleven years this Sunday, the 16th," said Bob standing up.

"Well, congratulations Bob. Did you two have a big church wedding?" asked Tom.

"We kept it super simple. We just went to the courthouse and had a Justice of the Peace do the deed," said Bob. "At the time my folks didn't think Dana was the right one for me, so it was just simpler to have a civil ceremony. But they did come to the reception and everything is good now."

"Well, you two seem super happy together. You're always rushing home to see Dana. Any tips on keeping the sparks alive?" asked Tom. "Amy and I haven't been on the same page lately and I could use some fresh ideas."

Bob sat back down. "To be honest, it hasn't always been easy. We've had our struggles. We seemed to have so much in common when we were dating…you know, our goals and values…what we wanted out of life. But about three years into our marriage things got pretty rough and we talked about splitting up. I got on a website called divorceprobability.com and from answering a few questions I discovered we were in real trouble."

"So, what did you do?" asked Tom.

Bob smiled. "What do you think I did? I'm a data guy Tom so I began researching what made for a great marriage."

Tom leaned in curiously, "What did you find? I'm all ears."
"There's a lot of data out there and some conclusions are kind of wonky," said Bob.

"Like what?" asked Tom curiously.

"Oh, I think the most interesting one is that there actually is data that shows that people who live in a city that has a major league baseball team have a 28% lower divorce rate than those who live in cities without a major league team. So, Dana and I turned 'interesting' into 'actionable' and moved to Denver," said Bob as he smiled.

"Wait...what?" said Tom.

Bob smiled. "So, here's the data on Denver. In 1990, a year before Denver was awarded a major league baseball franchise, the city's divorce rate stood at six divorces per 1,000 people. Ten years later, and seven years after the Colorado Rockies played their first game at the old Mile High Stadium, the divorce rate had declined 20 percent to 4.2 divorces per 1,000 people. In contrast, the overall U.S. divorce rate dropped only 15 percent."

"That's so funny. But seriously, what else did you find?" asked Tom.

"Gee, I haven't thought about this in a while but here's what we found to be actionable from the data. There's a researcher named John Gottman out of the University of Washington. He created something called 'a love lab' where he can observe, behind one-way glass, how couples interact with each other. He claims that after watching couples interact for just fifteen minutes, he can predict with 94 percent accuracy, who will be divorced, based on how one responds to their partner's, what he calls 'bids,'" said Bob. 'Bids' are invitations for connection. It's turning toward the bidder, not away from the bidder. Dana and I translated that into our relationship by committing to saying 'yes' to one another—leaning toward, not away from each other. So, if I ask Dana to get me a glass of water at 3 in the morning, the answer is 'yes,' not 'Get your own dang water.' If Dana asks me to clean up the kitchen before I go to bed, the answer is 'yes.' It was really hard at first, since you find out how really selfish you are but now it's quite a beautiful thing to have such a connection and since it is mutual, it tends to work really well for us."

"That's good, Bob. What else did you learn?"

"I came across some research out of the University of Virginia that demonstrated that couples who have a weekly date night report a 35 percent higher level of marital satisfaction. So, based on that research Dana and I put a weekly date night on the calendar. For us it is Saturday night. So, we usually go to dinner and maybe take in a play or a concert or sometimes we just walk on 16th Street."

"Yeah, that's something Amy and I used to do but then life gets busy," said Tom.

"I'm just telling you what's working for us," said Bob. "I've got to watch my Padres' guy, Manny Machado, then I probably ought to head for home," said Bob early into the top of the ninth inning.

Machado lined a single into deep right field advancing teammate Fernando Tatis to second base. "Well, I'll stick around and see what happens to Machado," Bob said.

"Before you go, is there anything else you learned about improving your marriage?" Asked Tom.

"Oh, yeah, one more thing. The importance of a daily six-second kiss. This is another Gottman finding. A six-second kiss is long enough to release oxytocin into the bloodstream. Oxytocin is the chemical that gives us the feeling of connection and intimacy with our mates. So, before we are out the door for work, we embrace and have a six-second kiss. And it's a good barometer of our relationship. If Dana doesn't want to kiss me I take it as a data signal that there is a breech in our relationship that we need to repair. So, it's hard to go more than a day or two being out of fellowship with each other," said Bob. "And I think I may have read something about the value of an eight-second hug but can't remember."

"That's really good Bob. I haven't heard any of this before. It's super helpful," said Tom. "You've really given me hope."

"We all need hope, Tom," said Bob.

Padres' Eric Hosmer's single drove in both Machado and Tatis. Rockies 11, Padres 7. Bob stood up to leave. "It's been a good evening, Tom. I've enjoyed your curiosity and questions and..." Bob's words were interrupted by the crack of the bat. Bob and Tom looked down at the field quickly enough to see Hunter Renfro's ball drive deep over the left field fence, driving in Eric Hosmer. Rockies 11, Padres 9.

Bob sat back down. "Well, now I better stay until the end of the inning to see what happens next. This is getting really interesting...and actionable."

By the time the ninth inning was over, the score was tied at eleven. There would be extra innings. In the 11th inning Tom took out his iPhone and took a picture of the scoreboard. The score was 11-11 at 11:11pm. Would the Rockies hold on? Could the Rockies hold on? Fewer than half of the original 38,000 fans who had stayed at the game were about to find out.

The twelfth inning proved to be a big inning for the Padres. Fernando Tatis led off with a triple into the left field corner, followed by doubles from Austin Allen and Manny Machado and a home run from Hunter Renfro, his third one of the evening. By the time carnage ended, the Padres had scored five runs and were now leading the Rockies, 16-11. The announcers called it "The Miracle in Denver."

As Rockies' first baseman Daniel Murphy, popped out for the last out for the Rockies, Bob said, "Fiero! I think we witnessed history tonight Tom. I'm really glad we stuck around. That's got to be one of the greatest, miraculous comebacks of all time and we were here to see it. We just witnessed an epic win." Tom and Bob high-fived each other and headed for the exit.

"Happy anniversary!" yelled Tom. "Give my best to Dana."
Bob waved his hand in acknowledgement as he headed down the escalator.

As Tom walked home, he reflected on the evening...the consultation, the marriage advice, the epic win. Earlier in the evening he identified himself with the Padres..."screwed!" But they made a miraculous comeback, defying all odds and won the game. Was it even possible he might do the same?

At home
When Tom came through the door, Tom was hoping Amy was still up, but it was nearly 11:30 and she and Riley were sound asleep.

After Tom and Amy had their morning workout, Tom suggested they walk down to Snooze and get a little breakfast. As Amy was finishing her egg white scramble, Tom took the conversation a bit deeper. "Amy, we both want to have a better marriage. So, I was thinking of that Bible passage in Revelation of what we need to do when we lose our first love."

"'...do the thing you did at first,'" said Amy.

"That's what I was thinking. So, remember how, before we had kids, we used to have a weekly date night? We did it come hell or high water—even during finals week in seminary. I'd like us to do that again. May I take you to dinner and a movie tonight?" Tom said with a smile.

"I think I'm free," said Amy hopefully.

Tom went on to tell Amy about the power of a daily eight-second hug and a six-second kiss. "Why don't we start with an eight-second hug," suggested Amy.

After the bill was paid, Amy and Tom stepped outside of the restaurant and Tom stepped in front of Amy and wrapped his arms around her waist. "I like your suggestion about starting with an eight-second hug."

"Here? With the world watching?" asked Amy.

"Sure, why not?" said Tom. "I mean we are married after all."

"Okay...but just watch out where your hands go," said Amy teasingly.

Chapter nine

At church

Sunday service went well though weekend attendance was lighter than Tom had hoped for, but it was the end of June after all and people were off on vacation. Nehemiah 7 would never be voted into the Top 100 chapters of the Bible, but it was about the census Nehemiah took of all the people in Jerusalem. To Tom, Nehemiah 7 was the transitional, bumper chapter that separated Nehemiah rebuilding the wall and Nehemiah rebuilding the people. So, just as Nehemiah had physically walked around the city to get a feel for the city in chapter two, he also took an assessment of the people to get a feel for the people of Jerusalem in chapter seven. Know and match...Know and match kept running through his mind. I've got to know about people in the city and people in the church to match them to their next step with God. Know and match.

Stephanie gave the results of the food drive which had exceeded her expectation. "Jesus said, 'the things I do, you shall do also,' and I'm happy to announce that this week we collected enough food to feed five thousand children one meal, or thirty-one kids for every day of this next school year." Tom was so proud of Stephanie and the work she had done.

After the second service, Harold walked briskly towards Tom. "Tom, it is church policy that any fund-raising or efforts like this be cleared through the elders, especially since giving is going down, we've got to coordinate how and when we ask our church to give." Harold may have had a point but Tom had a hard time receiving it. It just sounded like another criticism.

At church in the all-hands meeting

On Monday morning, at the all-hands meeting, Jerome, the Director of Spiritual Formation led the staff in the devotional out of 2 Chronicles 2. Nervously, Jerome began, "Last week the African American community celebrated Juneteenth to commemorate the day the slaves in Texas were told that they were free—some two years after the Emancipation Proclamation. That piece of data was withheld for two years...and that's not right." Jerome looked for a friendly face. "Tanika, would you please read verses 17 and 18?"

"Sure," said Tanika and turning to her YouVersion on her phone, she read,

> Solomon took a census of all the foreigners residing in Israel, after the census his father David had taken; and they were found to be 153,600. He assigned 70,000 of them to be carriers and 80,000 to be stonecutters in the hills, with 3,600 foremen over them to keep the people working.

"What's the Bible saying here?" Jerome asked rhetorically. This passage is about slavery—one man in power, dehumanizing all the foreigners in the land and conscripting them through forced, back-breaking labor to build Solomon's palace and God's temple. And that's how it's always been. It's the slaves who built the Great Wall of China, the pyramids of Egypt, the Taj Mahal, the White House, the University of Virginia—all built by slave labor. But what really gets me about this passage is that it was Solomon, who was supposed to be the wisest man of his time, that did such a stupid, de-humanizing thing and by doing so, gave implicit permission for God's people to enslave others because it was 'biblical.' The church has been complicit in perpetuating racism. It's so confusing." There he had said it.

Tanika dabbed her eyes with her index finger. Jerome continued, "Obviously I feel passionate about black lives and racial injustice but the point I want to make this morning is that data is neutral and can be used to accomplish great good and great evil. Can we stack hands as a church staff and agree to only gather information on or from people that advances God's purposes in their lives?" Jerome held his right hand forward. He was speaking literally about stacking hands. One by one the staff joined him at the front of the room and began stacking hands and with hands together began praying...for forgiveness, for insight...for repentance.

Tom felt so ignorant and vulnerable. Jerome had done his job that morning as Director of Spiritual Formation. He had afflicted the comfortable, and that was a good thing. Tom opened his calendar app and typed the words "Celebrate Juneteenth" on June 19 of 2020.

After a quick break Tom handed out a poster-sized, printed template. The template had spaces for the problem the teams were attempting to solve, their hypothesis for change, along with the experiment they'd run. "What's most important here," Tom said, "is to record what you learned from your hypotheses and experiment, that way we'll know whether to persevere or pivot. You guys will do a great job."

At the elder meeting
The elder meeting on Tuesday fared no better for Tom than the May meeting had gone. Elder Curtis White gave the devotional on Malachi 3—"I am the Lord. I changeth not!" Oh dear, thought Tom. Harold reminded Tom that attendance was slipping and chastised him for preaching a social gospel. Tom was behind the count and was down by several runs but as Harold had reminded him, he did have three more months to turn the ship around. He had seen a miracle at Coors Field with the Padres' comeback. Could God do it again? he thought.

Driving home from the elder meeting Tom felt the freedom to admit he was probably going to lose his job. What began as a feeling of freedom, degenerated into a mild panic attack. I'll get through this, Tom thought. God, help me get through this. Show me what to do.

At home
Amy got off the couch to greet Tom as he came through the door. "Looks like it didn't go all that well Tommy," empathized Amy. "I think you could use one of those six-second kisses. Then you can tell me all about those clowns on the elder board."

Tom couldn't help but smile. He might have had a board meeting that sucked but things were looking up for his marriage. "I think I'd like that. I know I don't say it often enough, but I just couldn't do this without you. Just to have you here when I come home...well...we'll get through this together. But let's start with your day. Anything exciting happen at work today?"

"Well, you know how exciting commercial real estate can be. Oh, but Boulder County did approve the building permit for the Sunset property in Erie, which made the Swensons really happy."

"That's great news," said Tom. "They are such good people!"

Friday, June 28. Denver Rockies v. Los Angeles Dodgers

Tom had texted Bob earlier in the afternoon promising to buy the beer if Bob could meet 30 minutes before the game to talk about what Daybreak should be measuring. Tom arrived to find Bob already seated with two bags of Ballpark peanuts in his hands. "Here ya go Tom," said Bob as he tossed a bag Tom's way.

"Thanks for the peanuts. Been here long?" asked Tom as he stuffed his bag of peanuts into the drink holder.

"Beer here!" yelled the Beer Guy and Tom held up two fingers and passed a twenty dollar bill his way.

"Yeah, I got here early enough to get Cody Bellinger to autograph this baseball for my nephew out in L.A. He's a real fan and Bellinger is the real deal. So...how'd the elder meeting go on Tuesday?"

Tom adjusted his Astros ball cap to keep the sun out of his eyes and turned towards Bob. "Oh, it was pretty ugly, but I think I've worked it through. I'm just surprised how little it takes for people to turn on you. It's little wonder most pastors say they have no friends. But staff meetings have been going well and I think the idea of "Build-Measure-Learn" is really catching on. A couple weeks ago I gave them copies of *The Lean Startup* and they love it. The staff seem to be trying more stuff and when it doesn't work, they are very much up-front and share what they learned and what they will do next time. And we are well into testing our hypotheses around Attract, Get, Keep, Grow and Multiply. Staff will report out on the results and their learnings in a couple weeks," said Tom.

"So, I got your note about what you ought to be measuring at Daybreak Church. You want to get more specific?" asked Bob.

"I've been thinking about what numbers we should be tracking at church. I know churches have historically counted nickels and noses or butts, bucks and baptisms, as my kids used to say, but from stuff I've been reading lately those three measures are increasingly ridiculed...but I haven't seen a good alternative. So, I was hoping, from your work with businesses that you might have some advice on what we should be tracking and measuring."

"When we asked the same question of ourselves back at Datanadec, the CIO had these t-shirts printed up when, as a company, we were trying to figure out the critical few things we wanted to measure." Tom looked at the white letters on the black T-shirt.

"WHAT GETS MEASURED, GETS DONE." PETER DRUCKER

"So, at Datanadec we learned to distinguish between what are called 'vanity metrics' and 'sanity metrics'—metrics that really identified if we were winning or not. Those are called Key Performance Indicators or KPIs."

"I've heard that term, 'KPIs,' before, but I mean we already have mission, vision, purpose, values, blah, blah…" said Tom. "Where do KPIs fit in?"

"Well, of course your mission statement is your reason you exist. The Key Performance Indicators are those few things you need to do and track to win at fulfilling your mission. They are quantifiable, outcome-based statements and always include a target, a measure, a data source and cadence of reporting. Ideally our KPIs help us focus on what matters and helps us measure progress towards fulfilling our mission. Get the KPIs right and the mission takes care of itself. Uh, I don't want to put you on the spot Tom, but do you have Daybreak's mission statement memorized?" asked Bob.

"Actually, I do. It's the first thing we worked on when I got here. We have all the staff memorize it. 'We exist to lead people into a relationship with Jesus, grow them into disciples, and equip them to be on redemptive mission in the city and in the world.'"

"That's one heck of a mission statement. I'm pretty impressed. So, you've got three or four things there…leading people to Jesus, growing disciples and equipping those disciples to make a difference in the world. So, your KPIs should inform you how you're making progress towards your mission. If a metric isn't attached to your mission it is probably a 'vanity metric.'"

"'Vanity metric?'" asked Tom.

"Well vanity metrics are metrics that might make you feel good but mean very little. So, for a company a vanity metric might be millions of page views or 'Likes' on your Facebook page. Vanity metrics don't offer any insight into how we got to where we are or any clue of what to do next," said Tom.

"What's the opposite of a vanity metric?" asked Tom. "What did you call them?"

"At Datanadec we called them 'sanity' metrics because they are the kind of metrics that help you make better decisions. 'Sanity' is defined by reason and rationality. So, sanity metrics are the kind of metric that ties specific actions to specific results. So great companies like Airbnb don't measure page views, they measure 'room nights rented' because the most important action they want to measure and multiply is room nights rented. That's what keeps them in business. That's how they measure if they are winning or not," said Bob.

Bob and Tom stood for the National Anthem and after sitting down Bob pointed to the scoreboard in left-center field. "That's the Rockies' scorecard you're looking at that tells the world if they are winning or not. At any time in the game every player, coach, manager, fan or peanut guy can look up there and figure out how the Rockies are doing and how they got to where they are. Those are the Rockies' KPIs...inning by inning, pitch by pitch, hit by hit, error by error, player by player, run by run. At any point in time the scoreboard tells them if they are winning or not and how many innings they have left to achieve their goal. I think that every data visualization tool seeks to be as good at telling the data story as well as a big-league scoreboard. No vanity metrics...all KPIs."

"Wow! That's what I need," said Tom. "A simple scorecard that gives me just enough information to let us know if we are winning or not."

The Dodgers started strong, building up a 3-0 lead going into the bottom of the second inning. Nolan Arenado brought the score within one run after launching a home run over the left field fence driving in Charlie Blackmon. Tom felt comfortable enough to restart the KPI conversation. "So, what do you think we should be measuring Bob?" asked Tom.

"There are a lot of things you could measure Tom, but I think for a church there are only five metrics that really matter that tell you if you are winning or not. If you track and grow these five numbers you will do just fine," Bob said.

"Let me guess," said Tom. "Are they Attract, Get, Keep, Grow and Multiply?"

"Of course, they are. How could I suggest that the church's operating system is Attract, Get, Keep, Grow and Multiply and then ask you to measure something else?" Bob said with a smile. "I like the idea of your KPIs being attached to the number of people you're attracting, getting, keeping, growing and multiplying, because all of these motions are tied to your mission and all can be actionable."

"I'm all ears," said Tom.

"I'll start with 'Attract,' which is really the hardest metric to actually measure. Attract is about the number of people who know you exist and what comes to mind when they think of you. That's a bit tough to measure but there is a decent proxy measure you can use."

"What's that?" asked Tom.

"If nearly one hundred percent of people who visit your church have visited your church's website, then visitors to your website is the first metric you want to track. Your website is your new front door, or 'screen door,' where people can invisibly check you out. So, you want to put your best foot forward. And with tools like Google Analytics, you can track your visitors, see how long they were on your site, what site they were on before they visited your site, etc. So, to make this actionable, this week you could start tracking the number of unique identities who visited your church's website compared to the actual number of new people who physically identified themselves as visitors at church. Then, if you have the desire and capacity, you can adjust your website to see if you can increase the number of people who visit your website and the percentage of people who make the move from being a digital lookie-loo to actually visiting your church," said Bob.

"That's good," said Tom.

"And if your goal is to move them from Attract to Get you will want to remove as much friction as possible by clearly displaying service times, where visitors can park, information about child check-in and even how to dress for those who haven't been to church in a while. So, start by measuring and increasing your digital impact on your website."

"I think I've got some people who can do that," said Tom. "So, what do we track around 'Get?'"

Bob thought for a second and then began. "'Get' is about getting people in the front door for the first time to a church service or event so you want to track first-time guests. I know that's tough since most folks who visit a church don't identify themselves until after a third or fourth visit but tracking first-time guests is super important. Some churches will motivate visitors to identify themselves by announcing that they are donating $10 to an anti-trafficking ministry or the local women's shelter if guests just text "GUEST" to a phone number. This way they capture the cell phone of the guest and can begin a communication sequence. Other churches use cellular geofencing to estimate the number of guests they have on the church campus at any one time. But one way or another first-time guests are critical to the future of any church., whether they visit in person, live online or on demand at some time during the week."

"We talked a lot about this at the Phillies game," said Tom. "So, if most visitors come to church because they are invited shouldn't that be a number we need to grow?"

"Good insight Tom," said Bob. "That may be the one critical metric you want to track and grow because without an infusion of new people a church is on a death spiral no matter how well it is doing in worship or discipling or missions. Churches lose an average of...something like 15 percent of their people each year due to attrition. You know, people move, die, switch churches, etc., so you need to replace those 15 percent each year just to maintain what you currently have. Those new people come from the 'Get' motion. My dad used to say, 'It's not what you do best that determines the future of your church but what you do worst that determines your future."

"What do you mean? What you do worst?" asked Tom.

"Well, you might have great teaching, worship, discipleship, have everyone in small groups and your building paid off but if you have not attracted anyone under the age of 35 you're dead in the water. That means in 20 years you have no one under 55 years old."

"That's crazy. No wonder so many churches close each year," said Tom.

By the top of the fourth inning the score hadn't changed. Dodgers 3, Rockies 2. "Do you mind if we keep talking about KPIs? I felt like we were just getting started," said Tom.

"Sure. Now...where were we? I think I was just getting to 'Keep,'" said Bob. "So, keeping people is super important. 'Keeping' is about keeping those you get and about closing the back door. If your front door is bigger than your back door you will grow but if more existing people are leaving than new people are joining you...well, I think you get where I'm going. Some people say that visitors return because they feel welcome but stay because they are valued. But you'd have to test that yourself. In business the rule of thumb was that the cost of getting a customer was five times as expensive as retaining an existing customer. I imagine it's not that different in the church world. I'd say tracking attendance falls under 'Keep.' What do you think attendance measures, Tom?"

"Well, I guess attendance indicates how many people are attracted to our mission and our message at Daybreak," answered Tom.

"I think so Tom. So, how might tracking attendance week after week become 'actionable?'" asked Bob.

Tom thought for a moment. "Well, I guess if attendance is going up it might mean that more people are attracted to what we do...you know...we are scratching where they are itching...that people actually want what we have and maybe that they are inviting their friends. So that might cause us to 'excel still more' in what we are doing. And I suppose if attendance is going down or plateauing, it probably indicates that we're not connecting with people in a way that creates value for them. So, since people tend to vote with their feet, attendance creates a good feedback loop."

Bob smiled. "I realize that attendance may seem like a lame measurement to some folks. And I'll be the first to say attendance doesn't equal engagement, but engagement almost always involves attendance. Can you ever think of a time in any church when declining attendance indicated things were getting better?"

Tom chuckled. "That's a good point Bob. So, we track website visits, first-time visitors, weekly attendance... 'Attract,' 'Get' and 'Keep.' So, what would you measure for 'Grow?'

Bob turned the question back to Tom, "What do *you* think you should measure Tom?"

Tom thought for a few moments and then said, "I don't know if this is what you mean but it's probably important to track the most important step in the growth journey—you know...people coming to Christ. I mean, we say 'we exist to lead people to Christ and grow them into disciples,' I guess that begins with measuring how many people we are introducing to Christ. I mean if we're not bringing more and more people into the family of God we might as well call ourselves a club rather than a church."

"I like that," said Bob. "So how can that metric become actionable?"

"Well, if we are not seeing people come to Christ...well, we'd need to change that...somehow," Tom replied. "We just don't want to gather discontented believers from other churches."

"Right. You may not know exactly what you need to do but I'm certain you could come up with hypotheses and experiments to try," said Bob.

"Yeah, um, yeah...we could do that," said Tom.

"So, what else might you want to track under 'grow?'" asked Bob.

"Well, at Daybreak we believe that people grow in the context of healthy relationships and like you say, it is 'relationships that catalyze growth,' so I think we need to measure new people joining groups, new groups started...things like that. People don't grow much in isolation. My pastor friend in Las Vegas says that 'Every unconnected believer is just one life event away from never being at your church again.'" said Tom.

"That's right on Tom," said Bob. "Small groups really are a spiritual catalyst. Believers in small groups learn more, serve more and give more. The more intentional a church is about small groups the greater the spiritual vitality of that church and the greater life change. Just getting people into small groups puts them on a moving sidewalk where a lot of good things happen."

The bottom of the fifth inning was huge for the Rockies and entertaining for the Rockies' fans. Down 5-2 at the beginning of the inning, the Rockies scored eight runs in the fifth inning on nine hits to lead the Dodgers 10-5. Rockies' right fielder Charlie Blackmon set an MLB record that night, getting three hits in each of six consecutive games. "I like how much sense this KPI stuff makes," said Tom. "But before we split can we talk about 'Multiply' as a KPI?"

"This one is actually the easiest KPIs to measure because there are so many ways a person can be a multiplier," said Bob. "I don't know if you remember this or not but 'multiply' was about those people who are *multiplying* the mission of the church, not just being recipients of the mission of the church. They've made the binary switch from being a *consumer* of the mission to being a *contributor* to advance the mission of the church. And they can do this through their giving over $500 a year to the church…."

"Where did you get that $500 number?" asked Tom.

"It comes out of one of those generosity consultancies. They classify as 'giver' as one who gives over $500 a year to their church. They say something like a third of church attendees give nothing to the church in a given year; another third of folks give between $1 and $499 but the majority of the church's work is sustained and advanced by people who give over $500 a year," said Bob. "They are multiplying the mission through their giving."

"I hadn't heard that before," said Tom.

Bob continued, "Or they can multiply the mission of the church through *leading* a small group or ministry…or through being the hands and feet of Jesus by *serving* in ministries in the church or in the community…or *inviting* people to church or through *evangelism* or *discipleship*. All this is very binary so it's super simple to count. Ideally you want to work towards 100 percent of your people at Daybreak contributing to advance the redemptive mission of the church through one or more of giving, leading, serving, etc. They would all be 'multipliers.' They would all be engaged in redemptive mission, which is the final part of your mission statement. These happy folks are actually engaged in fulfilling the mission of the church. If I could measure just one motion from the Church Engagement Framework, I'd probably track the folks who move from consumers to contributors…the multipliers who are, in one way or another, helping to fulfill the mission of Daybreak."

"Yeah," Tom paused. "That'd be a good KPI. That's a high bar but it totally makes sense," said Tom. "Do you have one of your cards so I can write this stuff down?"

"I always have a card Tom…and here's a pen to go with it. But to be fair, there is one super-important KPI you need to track. Some people call it 'the tool of tools.'"

"Duh! We have to track giving," said Tom.

"You're right but why do you say that?" asked Bob.

"Well, without money, our ability to attract, get, keep, grow and multiply would be extremely limited and we could never fulfill our mission," said Tom.

"That's very insightful," said Bob. "And because you cannot sustain Attracting, Getting, Keeping, Growing and Multiplying without a healthy financial engine, it is your finances that allow you to fulfill your God-given mission. I know people say they don't like a church talking about money but if you take your mission seriously, you've got to take your money seriously. It's the one number that can expand or shrink your kingdom influence."

At the top of the 7th inning the game was postponed because of lightning. The Rockies still held onto their lead, 10-8. Although the guests in the upper deck were asked to get under cover, Tom and Bob were dry and comfortable in their seats. While Bob got up to get a couple beers before the concessions closed, Tom took the time to create his own scorecard. He wrote out Daybreak's mission statement, then he sketched out his scoreboard.

Mission: "We exist to lead people into a relationship with Jesus, grow them into disciples and equip them to be on redemptive mission in the city and in the world"					
Key Performance Indicators					
	ATTRACT	GET	KEEP	GROW	MULTIPLY	GIVING
	# OF VISITORS TO WEBSITE	# OF 1ST-TIME GUESTS	ATTENDANCE	NEW BELIEVERS/ # OF SM GRPS # IN SM GRPS	# OF PEOPLE CONTRIBUTING TO THE MISSION	TOTAL GIVING REVENUE
THIS WEEK						
THIS WEEK LAST YEAR						
YEAR TO DATE						
YEAR TO DATE 2018						

Bob handed Tom a Coors Light as Tom stood up to let Bob find his seat. "Thanks, so much Bob. Hey, let me show you what I sketched out while you were gone. It's my perfect scoreboard. I'd put this up against what the Rockies have out there any day of the week," he said pointing to the Rockies scoreboard. "It's not only what's happening today but also how we got to 'now.'"

Bob smiled and looked at what Tom had written. "Yeah, this is a great start, Tom. I like that you have your mission statement at the top. You've just defined the 'win.' And I really like the way you included 'this week last year' and 'year to date' last year. That's about trends. It's only by including that data that you can see if you're making progress...or not. Yeah, it's a great start. Well done."

Tom liked hearing the words "well done." Those words didn't come to him that often at church, so it felt extra good to be acknowledged by someone as accomplished as Bob.

By the bottom of the eighth inning the Dodgers were gaining on the Rockies and were down by only one run, 10-9. But the Rockies were not going to let this victory slip away, adding three runs on three hits to pull away from the boys in blue, 13-9.

It had been a good evening, thought Tom as he walked home. He liked the idea of a one-page scorecard and thought the staff would like it too.

At home

"I'm home Amy," said Tom enthusiastically as he walked into their apartment. "And, come here you little furry-faced fluffy dog," he said as he bent over and scooped up Riley.

"Come and sit down next to me. So, what did you and Bob talk about tonight?" asked Amy.

Tom sat down on the couch and eagerly took Amy through his newly-developed church scoreboard. What a contrast in Tom's mood returning from a time with Bob compared to returning from an elder meeting. "Death and life are in the power of the tongue" she found herself thinking. Bob gave life to Tom. Harold was killing Tom's spirit.

"Ready for another episode of *The Crown* or did you have something else in mind?" she asked as she took Tom's hand.

Chapter ten

At church

It was the Fourth of July weekend and the Sunday morning attendance was light once again this Sunday. Tom's sermon was titled, "The joy of the Lord is your strength," from Nehemiah 8. Ezra reads through and explains the five books of Moses and when the people start mourning and lamenting because of the conviction they feel, Nehemiah tells them it is actually time to celebrate because they now know how God wants them to live. Tom reminded his flock that guilt may produce short-term religious conformity but only the joy of the Lord could fuel a lifetime walk with the Lord. Tom concluded his sermon with Nehemiah's admonition—"On this holiday weekend, 'go and enjoy choice food and sweet drinks, and send some to those who have nothing prepared. This day is holy to our Lord. Do not grieve, for the joy of the LORD is your strength." His application was met with universal smiles with the exception of Harold who was dismissively scribbling notes on his bulletin.

Upon stepping down from the raised platform after the first service, Harold handed Tom a note, "I think it was very inappropriate not to have an American Flag on stage today on 4th of July weekend. And we should have sung 'God Bless America.' It's in the hymn book for a reason."

At church in the all-hands meeting

It was Monday morning and as Tom was driving to the church, there was one question that plagued him. "How can we make it as easy to contribute as it is to consume?" Facebook had figured it out. Contributing to a post by hitting the "like" button was actually easier than consuming a post. How can I flip the script? he thought.

The energy and banter among the staff at the all-hands meeting was palpable. How different than when I first arrived, thought Tom. Susie, the office manager was on deck for the morning devotional. A native Kentuckian, Susie had been leading a global student ministry in Boston before making the move with her husband to Colorado a few months before Pastor Arnie had died. She was an eager and life-long learner and Tom always looked forward to what she had to say.

"I finished Eric Ries' *Lean Startup* this week and was captured by the concept of A/B testing, where we pit one solution against another to see which takes us closer to our goal. Once I understood the concept I began thinking of A/B testing like the Sweet 16 brackets of the NCAA basketball tournament...Go Hilltoppers!...where one approach goes against another with the winner advancing to the finals. This concept is so critical to continuous improvement. And then this week I was reading in the Book of Daniel and am convinced that Daniel invented A/B testing."

"How's that?" asked Kaiya, the Middle School Director.

"Well, remember that Daniel made up his mind not to defile himself with the king's food and wine, so he proposed the following." Susie opened her Bible to Daniel 1.

"Daniel said, 'Please test your servants for ten days. Let us be given only vegetables to eat and water to drink. Then compare our appearances with those of the young men who are eating the royal food, and deal with your servants according to what you see.' So, at the end of ten days, Daniel and his men looked healthier and better nourished than all the young men who were eating the king's food.' That is the essence of A/B testing. I see a day coming very soon that rather than just running one experiment, we are testing multiple approaches and then measuring to see which is most effective. This is going to be so much fun. I can't wait!" Susie said enthusiastically.

"Thanks Susie," said Tom. "I get excited just hearing your vision for all of this."

Friday, July 12. Denver Rockies v. Cincinnati Reds
Tom was in his seat a little after 6pm for the Rockies game where they would face the Cincinnati Reds. He'd left home early enough to enjoy his steak and potato burrito and reminded himself to pick up two bags of peanuts from the vendor next to the burrito guy outside the stadium. "Two dollars here...five dollars inside" was still a good incentive. It was close to 80 degrees when Bob nudged Tom to signal that he was coming into the row. "Did you watch the Home run Derby on Monday?"

"It was crazy!" said Bob. "I remember when Josh Hamilton broke all the records back in 2008 by hitting...what was it...28 home runs? And we thought that was something. And now Guerrero hits like 40 in that second round? And all these guys are so young."

"Doesn't it seem like there are more home runs hit in the games too?" asked Tom.

"Oh, that's a fact. I mean when I was growing up my coaches would tell us not to swing for the fences. Now I think coaches are telling them *to* swing for the fences. Back in 1989 home runs were pretty rare...something like one in every twelve hits. Today it's something like one in every six hits. And I think it has something to do with data."

"Now you really have my attention," said Tom.

"I think it's what the NBA discovered about the 3-pointer—it's one and a half the value to a regular basket and the miss rate isn't that much different from shots inside the 3-point line. So now teams have figured out that a home run translates to at least one run and maybe even four runs. So, I think we'll see more home runs this year than we've ever seen. I mean we broke the May and June home run records," said Bob.

"And probably break more strikeout records too," added Tom.

"No doubt," said Bob. "It's been the trend for the past several years for sure."

"Well, we could sure use a few dingers in this game. I mean, losing the last six in a row. It's lucky we're sitting even with 45 wins...and 45 losses." Sitting down after singing the National Anthem, Tom turned to Bob. "So, what's up with your T-shirt? I thought we were supposed to 'start with why?'" said Tom. "I mean that's what Simon Sinek says."

Bob looked down at his black T-shirt.

START WITH "HOW"

"Yes, of course. Your 'Why' is super important but if you get your 'HOW' right the 'why will fall into place," said Bob. "I guess I should explain. When I started with Datanadec back in the 90's we had all these aspirational slogans plastered all over the walls about Datanadec being the premier this and that...to be world class...to dominate the competition...be the most-admired...blah, blah blah. It was all about us and it showed. We were arrogant towards our clients. In fact, we'd often joke that arrogance was our strength. We treated our customer like it was their privilege to work with us young Turks, so they repaid us by not renewing their contracts and not recommending us in spite of the fact we had a ground-breaking data and analytics product. Internally, the drive to be the best took its toll. We had leaderboards, publicly stack-ranking our sales staff with the bottom twenty percent terminated each quarter. Our directors and managers drove people to meet their numbers and that took its toll on all employees. I guess we'd say today that we had a toxic culture."

"Sounds like a disaster," Tom said. "So, what happened then? How'd you turn it around?"

"Well, we were pretty desperate, so we hired a consultant who specialized in cultural turn-arounds. Yeah, a super smart guy, George Kopak, with the consulting group Wong and Wright out of the City and mentors young entrepreneurs at Cal. He spent three weeks interviewing employees, looking over the financials...talking to current and lapsed customers. Then came the 3-day offsite up in Napa Valley, at a hotel in a little town called Yountville, that overlooked the vineyards. Great place for an offsite. We had no idea what George was going to tell us," Bob said.

Although they didn't realize it until later, Bob and Tom were witnessing history. In all the MLB games ever played this was the first time the two starting pitchers had the same last name. Jon Gray was on the mound starting for the Rockies and Sonny Gray was the starting hurler for the Reds. And both pitchers were at the top of their game, matching not only their surnames but their pitching prowess in this epic showdown. By the top of the third, neither of the Grays had given up any runs.

As good as the game was, Tom was anxious to get back to conversation about the offsite. "Well, so what happened at the offsite up in Napa?"

"Well on the first day...after starting with lunch, there were about twenty of us with the management team all seated around a big conference table and the others who had joined us seated against the walls. George got up in front of the white board and said something like, 'I'd like to be able to tell you that you're doing okay…but you're not doing okay. Customer churn is high, employee satisfaction is low, sales are declining, renewals are in the tank, and customer service is woefully lacking. If nothing changes you will be out of business in eleven months. That's the bad news.' You could have heard a pin drop in the room. We weren't prepared for such a shocking report. Our CEO perked up and asked, 'What's the good news?' George answered with earnest enthusiasm. 'First, you have great people in the company. They are bright, talented and hard-working and want to be here. Second, you have an amazing product—your data gathering, analytic tools and processes are second-to-none in creating proven value for your clients. Your proprietary ability to help clients visualize their data to make their data actionable is a breakthrough product. But you're missing one thing." Well, of course that caused everyone in the room to perk up and lean in. So, our COO spoke up and said, 'So if we have great people and a great product, what are we missing?' Bob paused.

"Well, what did he say? How'd he answer?" asked Tom with anticipation.

"I've got to use *el baño* and was thinking about grabbing something to drink, so we can talk about it when I return. What do you think he told us? Give it some thought." With that Bob headed up the stairs towards the nearest Men's Room and then to the nearest concession stand.

"Here ya go Tom," Bob said as he handed Tom his drink before slipping past him into his seat. "Pass me one of those bags of peanuts, would you?" Tom readily complied.

By the top of the sixth inning, it was clear that the pitching Grays were determined not to be outplayed by their patronymic doppelganger. Each complete inning averaged a total of only seven batters and the score remained…Rockies 0, Reds, 0.

Breaking the tension, Bob kept his eyes on the mound but turned to Tom and asked, "So, did you figure out what was missing at Datanadec?" Tom looked at him with a bit of helplessness. "Well, I couldn't figure it out either," said Bob. "But George said that we could be leading the market in the next year if we just got one more thing right. He said we have the people and the product but what we lacked was found in our…priorities. Priorities, he explained were about 'what comes first' and we were putting ourselves first rather than putting our customers first. That's when he turned around and wrote, on the whiteboard in all caps, H-O-W. 'You will completely turn your company around by practicing H-O-W; *Helping Others Win*. If you put HOW into practice within Datanadec, helping each employee win and with your clients, helping them to win, you will end up winning as a company.' Well, of course there was some pushback. In fact, our H.R. Director was gone by the end of the day and our COO was gone by the end of the offsite but over the course of the next two days we crafted a plan that created a *Help Others Win* culture, within the company, with our vendors and with our customers."

Tom was fascinated. He felt like he was on the inside watching the wheels of high tech turning and he wanted to know more. "So, what were the big take-aways?"

"The big idea George unpacked for us is that every human being is trying to accomplish something. He drew up Maslow's hierarchy of motivation on the whiteboard. At the most basic even most primitive level people are trying to win at the survival level...the food, clothing and shelter and at the highest level they are trying to win at 'self-actualization.' I've never really cared for that word but it's the idea that people want to fulfill their God-given purpose and be what they were created to be. Every successful enterprise has figured out how to insert themselves between where people are and where people want to be...between what people have and what people want. At Datanadec we had it all backwards. In the extreme, managers were using employees to win to advance their own purposes. Our sales team was burning through prospects until prospects bought something, creating a win for that salesperson. We were using people to validate ourselves...to help *us* win. That was pretty clear."

"That sounds fascinating. Oh, to be a fly on the wall during those three days," said Tom. "So, what happened next?"

Bob was more than happy to respond. "George quoted an entrepreneurial friend of his who always says that the best way to be successful is to become a tactic in someone else's strategy, helping..."

"Helping others win," said Tom finishing Bob's sentence.

"That'd be right Tom. And George reminded us that we needed to start with those inside our own company. If we're not willing to eat our own dog food, and practice internally what we wanted to be externally we'd never be able to export this big idea. So, we spent Wednesday afternoon through mid-morning on Thursday working on what wins would look like for every employee at Datanadec. Early on we had a lot of debate about this but eventually started with categories outlined by Harvard's Human Flourishing Program. These six areas seem to be universal since in any place in the world flourishing people are thriving in six different areas. People around the world want to be happy, healthy, virtuous, financially secure, have good relationships and live with purpose. We chose those six areas because Harvard also identified four pathways to thrive in these six areas and 'Work' was one of those four pathways. So, the workplace is a natural place to help people thrive. Our company, if structured right, can be a tactic in other people's strategy to thrive. We created a worksheet called "The Top Six" where twice a year each employee defines what a "win" would look like for them in each of these six areas. Now it becomes the manager's job to help them win in each of these areas."

"So how did it go?" asked Tom.

"Turnover went waaaay down, our Glassdoor reviews were close to 5 stars and for the last five years I was there, Datanadec was named as one of the Top Ten tech companies to work for in the Bay Area," said Bob with a touch of pride. "And all that crap we had on the walls about 'We are the best this and the best that...whatever' was taken off and replaced with a simple graphic in the reception room, every conference room, every breakout space and every workstation...'Help Others Win.' Everything we do as a company is built around those three words-- 'Help Others Win.' "

"Dang! That is so good Bob. I'm curious to hear what happened to sales and with all your clients," asked Tom.

"I guess this would be a good time to tell the rest of the Datanadec story."

"That'd be great," Tom said.

"Well, the first thing we did is to interview our top one hundred customers and asked *them* to define what their win was. So, our first job was simply to listen and learn."

Their conversation was interrupted to watch the replay of Reds' Jesse Winkler's triple that drove in teammate Curt Casali. The Reds had broken the spell and held a 1-0 lead going into the bottom of the 6th inning.

As Sonny Gray took the mound, Tom turned to Bob. "Did you see anything your customers had in common?"

Looking straight ahead at the pitcher's mound, Bob answered. "Yeah, it took us a while but through a lot of listening we discovered that for all of our clients, their 'wins' fell into five big buckets...they wanted *more* of something, like more customers...more sales and the like, *less* of something...less friction, less customer churn, etc., a *better* something...like customer experience, a *faster* something or a *cheaper* something. Through intentionally listening to what our customers are trying to accomplish we became really good at actually matching them to what we could do for them in the area of data, analytics, visualization and messaging. We learned more from them through that simple listening tour than all of us could have come up with on our own. So, we moved from how we can get you to buy what we have to 'What would be a win for you?' Followed by 'How can we help you win?' Just that simple approach changed everything for us. We had a very binary response to their win. If we had a solution that could help them win, we enthusiastically explained the benefits of working with us. If we couldn't help them win with our existing products or services, we pointed them to others who could help them win—sort of the Macy's-Gimbal's thing."

"From Miracle on 34th Street," said Tom.

"That's right," said Bob. "After all, our overarching goal was not to sell products but to help others win. We took a dip in our sales for about six months but taking the time to understand our customer's needs put us on the pathway to develop new product lines that meet our customer's needs better than our competitors. And when our customers bought our products, we gave them the assets and support they needed until they got the win they were looking for. Eventually we developed an automated process, but we had to do a lot of handholding in the beginning, but again, that's how we learned what a 'win' was for our customers. Our motto was, 'The sale is not complete until our customers win by getting what they paid for.' I think our customers really appreciated that and they were more than willing to tell their friends about us. Our Net Promoter Score was among the highest in the Bay Area. It was quite a ride. 'Helping Others Win' was really big for us. We've found the sweet spot of our market niche by helping others win. So that's why I say, 'Start with HOW.'"

In the bottom of the sixth first year Rockies' Daniel Murphy punched out a double, driving in David Dahl. Reds 1, Rockies 1. The pitching Grays were even once again.

"Sounds like one amazing ride. Sometimes I find myself feeling a bit jealous of all the great resources and the rate of learning that comes out of business and tech. Seems we as the church are always playing catch-up," lamented Tom.

"Well, that's not necessarily a bad thing. Let the for-profit folks spend their time and effort paying the dumb tax but once they figure things out then see what's valuable for you to adopt. And by the way, business leaders have a lot they could learn from you pastors. I mean I don't think a single one could do what they do...do what *you* do...using an all-volunteer work force to accomplish a life-changing mission," said Bob.

Tom sat up a little straighter. He hadn't felt that affirmed in quite a while and it felt good. "This is really helpful Bob. How do you see Helping Others Win being deployed in the church setting?"

"You've got to be...your church must figure out how to be...well...a tactic in people's strategy. People are rarely looking for church, but they are looking for things that your church provides. So, a 'win' for people is rarely 'I want to find a good church.' More likely people are looking for ways to make their lives work. As the Harvard flourishing study shows, a flourishing life consists of happiness and well-being, character and virtue, close social relationships, physical and mental health, financial stability and living from purpose and meaning. Those are the 'wins' every person is looking for," said Bob.

"So, you're saying that if we do this right, the church can become a tactic in every person's strategy to live a flourishing life...which is probably part of God's intention," pondered Tom slowly.

"Yeah, I think that's right. Remember when I was talking about Datanadec's Employee's Top Six Goal Sheet?" asked Bob. "And I also said that Harvard discovered that there are four 'pathways' to human flourishing among one of which was work. Do you want to know the other three pathways?"

"Don't tell me *church* is one of them?" asked Tom with anticipation.

"Yep...church is one of those four pathways. Harvard calls them 'religious communities' but for you it means 'church.' So, the four pathways to human thriving are family, work, education and religious community. So actually, Harvard did the heavy lifting of discovering how to be a tactic in every person's strategy. People may not be looking for church, but they are definitely looking for the things that churches can help them win at— close relationships, purpose, character development and the rest," said Bob. "Yeah, you're a pastor Tom but you're also a coach. You help people win in areas that are most important to them. You help your people and the people of Denver win Tom. And guess what? That's how you win."

Bob's words about being a coach and helping win were words Tom wanted to resonate with. "I can't tell you how helpful this has been Bob. My mind is just racing with ideas about how we might bring this into church."

"Just don't let any person diminish the role you and your church play in the well-being of Denver," Bob said. "It's like the words of that ancient epistle—'the Christian is to the world what the soul is to the body.' You and your church are absolutely essential to the well-being of your city. When a church leaves a city...part of the soul of the city disappears and a city without a soul is not a good place to live. I think this is what Mark Zuckerberg discovered a couple years ago when he went around the country visiting churches and interviewing pastors. He concluded that Facebook needs to be more like the church. Think about it, Facebook is becoming the place where members gather to comfort and encourage one another. They check in on the sick and struggling. They wish each other a happy birthday. They send out prayer requests, Scripture verses and Bible memes. They are set up to rejoice with those who rejoice and weep with those who weep. Zuckerberg figured this out. You might say Facebook is trying to become a tactic in people's strategy to live a full life. Crazy, huh? But that shows the power of ecotones."

"Oh, yeah...ecotones," said Tom hesitantly.

By the seventh inning stretch, the Reds had pulled ahead on the powerful one-run home run by lead-off batter, Eugenio Suarez. Reds 2, Rockies 1. Jon Gray quickly disposed of the next three batters. The grounds crew dragged the infield dirt as Tom and Bob stood, stretched their legs and belted out
     And its root, root, root for the Rockies (Tom sang "Astros"),
     If they don't win, it's a shame.
     For it's one-two-three strikes you're out,
     At the old ball game!

"'Ecotones?' I don't think I know that word," said Tom.

"I suspected so," said Bob. "I haven't met many people who have but it's a powerful concept found in nature. It is the space where two ecosystems intersect." Bob reached into his pocket and pulling out a 3x5 card drew two overlapping circles. "Ecotones are the intersections between ecosystems. It's an estuary where saltwater and freshwater meet and mingle. Its where the marsh and the grassland intersect, where the forest and grasslands intersect, between mountain forest and alpine life zone—any place where two

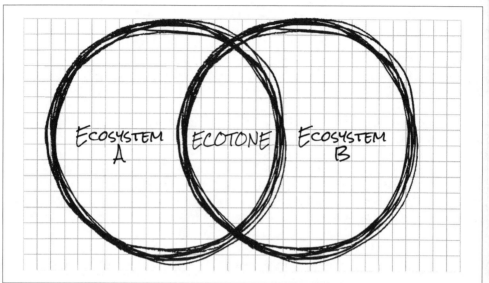

distinct ecosystems collide," said Bob as he began to draw two overlapping circles on one of his 3x5 cards.

"So, what happens in these ecotones?" asked Tom with curiosity.

"Well, for one thing there are more life species in ecotones than either of the adjacent ecosystems. It's where life adapts and evolves so there are unique life species that live in the ecotone that don't exist in either of the adjacent ecosystems. It is in ecotones where life happens and thrives, so scientist say that adaptation and growth happen only when the ecosystems come together. So, to me, in order to grow I need to intentionally put myself with others that swim in a different stream than I do if I want to grow," said Bob.

"So, how do you do that?" asked Tom.

"I think marriage is a great example." With that, Bob flipped the 3x5 card over and drew the two overlapping circles and labeled one circle 'Bob (Me)' and the other one 'Dana (You)" In the intersection, the ecotone, he wrote 'We.'

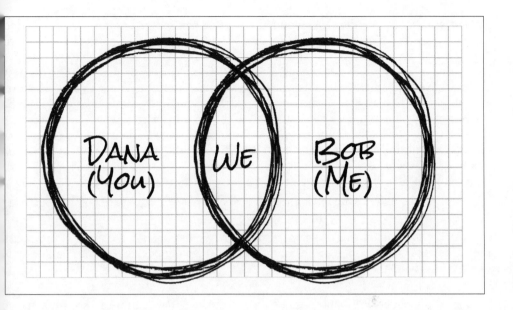

"So, when I was single, I was in my own ecosystem and there was little potential for adaptive growth and adaptive change. And one can be content within one's own ecosystem. But when we marry, we collide with another ecosystem and it is this ecotone that is the Petri dish for change and growth. "Me" and "you" become "we." I can't think about what's best just for my ecosystem—to make my life work and the same goes for Dana. We are forced through this collision to think about what makes "our" life work. Going back to the characteristics of ecotones. There is more 'life' here in this space," said Bob pointing to the intersection with his pen, "than in either of our lives individually. And there is a unique quality of life that exist here that doesn't exist when we are not together. And it is in the space of 'we' where change and growth occur. It is in this 'we' ecotone where the two really do become one."

Tom had never heard of such a thing before. The Reds' ace, Sonny Gray quickly disposed of the first three batters in the bottom of the 7th. Both Grays had been historically stellar that night but now it was time for the highly paid relief pitchers to step in.

Bob continued. "So, every Friday night you and I are together Tom, we create our own ecotone. There's a quality of life and an evolution of ideas that only happens when we are in this space. It's a very powerful concept and it builds a good case for church people to learn from others and for others, like Zuckerberg, to learn from church people. You might have half an idea and I might have the other half, but it is only through crossing the streams can the whole idea come to fruition. That's where good ideas come from. That's how the Renaissance came about by intermingling the best artists, architects, mathematicians and writers in the city of Florence. It's combining the wine press with metallurgy to produce the printing press."

Tom loved what he was hearing but did not expect what Bob said next.

"There's also an implication for churches Tom," said Bob. "As long as churches remain inside their walls, they, like a contented single, are not growing or changing and it's easy to think all is well, and the world is working according to plan. But once the church starts engaging in community, if it wants to transform a community, it must be willing to be transformed by the community as much as it wishes to transform a community. If a church is unwilling to grow and change as much as they want to change their city, it can never be an agent of transformation in the community. Without a degree of mutuality, a church just has an agenda. And people in the city sniff that out pretty quickly."

Tom took off his Astro's cap and fanned himself before wedging it back on his head.

It was a big evening for Rockies' Daniel Murphy, culminating in the bottom of the eighth inning he recorded his first home run as a Rocky, driving in David Dahl. The Colorado Rockies held on to their 2-1 lead.

Tom certainly never heard about ecotones in seminary. Bob continued, "So, Tom, you've been in Denver eight or nine months. How has the city changed you? How have you changed or grown since you moved here? What have you learned from people in the city about human flourishing?"

Tom searched for something offbeat or humorous to say to lighten the conversation and take the attention away from him but came up empty. "Well, I think we're not to conform ourselves to the patterns of this world. I think the people of God need to set the standard for people in the city."

"Okay, so that's what you bring to the city. What are the city's gifts to you? Who cares about Denver as much as you do, even though they may not be a Christ follower?" asked Bob. "What unlikely person in the city can change your life?"

Tom felt his face growing flushed and to politely end the conversation said, "Let me think about that Bob."

Two hours and forty minutes after Jon Gray threw his first pitch, the game was over—the second shortest game of the season. Tom walked home through the dispersing crowd. He consciously tried to think about how he could help others win but the gravitational pull of Bob's question was too powerful.... "What unlikely person in the city can change your life?" Lord, help me, he thought. No seriously, I'm willing...just a bit scared.

Coors Field was a mere two blocks away from his and Amy's residence in the Douglas Apartments and it didn't take long for Tom to cover the distance. The Denver Rescue Mission was just a block away from the Douglas Apartments, so homeless encampments and panhandlers were a familiar sight to Tom. Although he had never stopped and talked to any of the homeless, tonight, he determined, would be different. He'd have a conversation with the first panhandler that he would see. He kept his eyes on the heels of the person walking ahead of him.

Crossing Market Street on his usual route home, Tom had to look up as he stepped up the curb and found himself locking eyes with a slender figure, with a sad face with pierced lips slowly picking his guitar and singing Leonard Cohen's, "Hallelujah." If there was pain in the song, there was pain in the voice. Tom looked to the ground to see a neatly drawn cardboard sign propped up against an open guitar case.

RAISING DOWN-PAYMENT FOR A CHEESEBURGER

Tom smiled and for the first time in a long time reached into his pocket and put a five-dollar bill into the guitar case, then cautiously stepped backwards. Better not get too close. The guitarist smiled. Tom smiled back. Tom regretted his bargain with the Lord about "talking" with the first panhandler. He'd actually have to talk with this guy. The street musician finished singing about a cold and broken Hallelujah that sent a shiver through Tom's body.

There was eager applause and a few more people stepped forward to toss in some change or a dollar or two. Tom found himself standing next to the street musician. "Hey thanks man," said Francis. "It's been a long day."

"You're welcome. It's nothing. I mean it's just five bucks, and I loved the song," said Tom wanting to end the conversation.

"No, I didn't mean that," said Francis. "I mean thanks for the money and all but thanks for looking me in the eye and sticking around to hear my music and well...just acknowledging me as a human being. That hasn't happened much lately."

Tom was unsure of what to say, but thinking of Jesus' example, introduced himself. "Hey I'm Tom. What's your name?"

"Francis and my friends call me...well 'Francis.'"

"Nice to meet you Francis," said Tom with his hands in his front pockets, careful not to touch the man. "Mind if I ask you, what brought you to Denver?" Tom asked awkwardly.

"Oh, it's a long story," said Francis. "I guess it was a combination of love and hate. I loved a guy and when my dad found out, he kicked me out of the house and told me not to come back until I had gotten my act back together. But it wasn't an act. It was me he was against. I felt he really and truly hated me. So, my partner Travis and I said, 'screw this' and left

Cedar Falls and hit the road for Denver. He had a decent job as a graphic designer so for the first couple months, while I was looking for a job, it was great. Then he met someone else at work, dumped me and kicked me out of the condo. He just turned on me. Hard to get a job when you don't have an address. But it's all chill."

Dang! He was talking with a gay guy. He's probably going to ask if he can crash at our place, Tom thought. He probably thinks I'm gay. He had never knowingly had a conversation with a gay man before. Of course, there was his cousin Larry. But his family disowned him when he came out twenty years ago. "Nice meeting you Francis. Yeah, uh my wife's waiting for me so I'd better get home."

"Must be nice to have someone you love waiting at home for you. You are blessed," said Francis. "See you around."

"Yeah, see you around," said Tom as he turned to walk towards home. I can't believe a gay guy can feel so much pain after a breakup. I mean he can always hook up at a gay bar or get on one of those gay apps, Tom thought. I wonder if Larry's still alive?

At home
Amy was still up when Tom came through the door. "I had an amazing night tonight, Babe. Just a bunch of good things happened, starting with a Rockies' win. And Bob had some very helpful thoughts on helping others win and then I talked to this gay guy and now I'm home with you."

"What? I'm all ears. This sounds like it could be more interesting than *The Crown*. Pull down a couple of glasses and I'll get us something to drink."

Chapter eleven

At church

The Sunday service was upbeat and had gone smoothly. Attendance was up from the fourth of July weekend and Tom's message on Nehemiah 9, a chapter about the cycles of blessing, rebellion and chastisement had been well received. Tom paid special attention to verse 35. "Even while they were in their kingdom, enjoying your great goodness to them in the spacious and fertile land you gave them, they did not serve you or turn from their evil ways," emphasizing that, for a season, we can be far from God and still enjoy his goodness, but God has more for his people. Tom made liberal use of quotations from C.S. Lewis' *Mere Christianity* written in the throes of World War II. Tom's haymaker ending finished with a quote by Plato. "Be kind for everyone you meet is fighting a battle."

Between services Harold cornered Tom. "Brother, you need to not be quoting C.S. Lewis...all that nonsense about God shouting to us in our pain. Lewis was an evolutionist and is part of the Creation Museum's Wall of Shame. Lewis is banned from our school. We need to ground our students in a biblical worldview. You can't pick and choose which parts of the Bible are true or not. It will serve you well to leave him out of your sermon in the next service. And Plato? Come on." Tom nodded, not in agreement but in acknowledgement and changed nothing of what he said in the second service.

At church in the all-hands meeting

Tom looked forward to the all-hands meeting on Monday. It was time to report out on how their experiments had gone. After the usual chit-chat, Tom nodded to Renee, the Director of Women's Ministry to lead the staff devotional. Renee was a young mom in her mid-thirties and a student of the Bible and a curious learner.

"These past several weeks, as we've been running our experiments and experiencing the build, measure, learn cycle, I've been thinking...if this is a universal approach, where is this found in the Scriptures? That question took me to our old friend Solomon in the book of Ecclesiastes. And it shouldn't surprise us that we might find the Build, Measure, Learn cycle in the hands of King Solomon from back in the day. After all he gave us the maxim, 'What has been will be again, what has been done will be done again; there is nothing new under the sun.' So, let's take a look at how he employed and maybe even invented the Build, Measure, Learn cycle. So, what was he solving for in Ecclesiastes? In chapter 2 he tells us. 'I wanted to see what was good for people to do under the heavens during the few days of their lives.' So, he started experimenting—that's the Build phase. The text says he undertook great projects, built houses, planted vineyards, made gardens, parks and reservoirs. He bought slaves, herds and flocks and acquired silver, gold, treasures. Then he tried a pleasure trip...singers, a harem of beautiful women. He tried all the hedonistic pleasures of this life."

"That's the kind of experiment I'd like to get in on," an undistinguished voice said. Most everyone laughed.

Renee continued. "Then Solomon measured. He says, 'Yet when I surveyed all that my hands had done and what I had toiled to achieve, everything was meaningless, a chasing after the wind.' What did he learn? That 'nothing was gained under the sun.' So, what does he do? Remember, after learning the lessons of the experiment we decide whether to persevere...if it seems that we are getting the results we hoped for, or if the result we get refutes our hypothesis yet delivered valuable insight to what *doesn't* work, we pivot. So as Tom says, 'a pivot is not a change in the vision but a change in the strategy or tactic that will get us to the vision.' So, since Solomon's big question was to discover 'what was good for people to do during the few days of their lives,' it was time for Solomon to pivot. So, Solomon went back to the drawing board and built a number of successive Build, Measure, Learn experiments involving labor, time, friendship, job promotion, riches, wisdom, governance, humanity, providence, diligence, investment, youth and old age. With each experiment he measured the results and learned from his experiment—'No...that's not quite it, he'd say. So, he pivoted and tried another approach until he finally found his solution. He says, 'Here is the conclusion of the matter: Fear God and keep his commandments, for this is the duty of all mankind.' He found the sustainable business model for living life. If Solomon, apart from him enslaving the foreigners that Jerome enlightened us on, was among the wisest of the wise, couldn't get it right the first time, can we give ourselves the grace to experiment and through validated learning, which includes a lot of failure, get better and better? I mean the Bible hints that Jesus himself 'learned obedience through what he suffered.' Build, Measure, Learn. Let's pray that God would give us that same spirit as Solomon to build, measure and keep learning."

"That was very insightful. Thank you, Renee and of course it's a great segue to what we'll do this morning," said Tom, stepping up to his computer and finding his PowerPoint presentation, opened to the template he asked each team to fill out and send in.

Experiment #1 Outcomes		Date: __/__/____
What problem were you solving for? (Attract, Get, Keep, Grow or Multiply?) What is the concise statement of the problem you were trying to solve:	Hypothesis #1: "We believed, if we did _____ _____ _____, it would lead to more of / less of _____ _____ _____ (our desired outcome)"	Experiment #1 What you did: How you measured it: Results:
What would an "Epic Win" look like?	Notes:	What you learned: Persevere or Pivot (Circle one)

"Thanks for sending your slides to me. So, I'd like each team leader to introduce his or her team and then you have five minutes to walk us through your slide, starting with the problem you are solving for. Stephanie, tell us what you did with Attract."

Stephanie quickly introduced her team and then looked at the large monitor with her slide displayed in PowerPoint. "Our problem is around 'Attract.' How can we make more people in the city aware that we exist and what we are known for positively when they think of us? Our 6-month epic win would be wherever we go in the city, whoever we talk to, when we mention that we are part of Daybreak that people would respond, 'I've heard of you guys. I like what you're doing.'"

"That *would* be an epic win Steph," affirmed Dan.

"Our hypothesis was, 'If we are letting our light shine in the city, and the more Daybreak folks post about it on Facebook and Instagram, the greater positive awareness people in the city will have of our church. Our experiment was to ask our people to post the results of the Food Drive on Instagram and Facebook with the hashtag #noonehungry and a link to our food drive page on our website. We measured the total number of 'Likes' we had on our Facebook page and on our Instagram page, before and after the food drive and the unique visitors to our website after the campaign compared to what we were averaging. The results were pretty good. We had about 60 Daybreak folks post on Facebook or Instagram, which we thought could have been way higher. We got 270 more "Likes" on our Facebook page and 112 more on Instagram. Our big learning was that this actually worked but we screwed up on the hashtag. Most people read 'no one hungry' as 'noon-y-hungry' which made no sense. We could also be more specific on what to post...you know...give them some tips on what to say, or how their family participated and what it meant to them. And I think we could double the number of people who post the next time we do something like this. So, as you see, our plan is to persevere."

"Great work Steph and team," said Tom. "James you're up to tell us about 'Get,'" said Tom as he advanced to the next PowerPoint slide.

James introduced his team and then began. "We are solving for how we might double our number of first-time visitors by doubling the number of Daybreak Church people who invite someone to our service or event…from our normal 10 percent to 20 percent of our folks inviting someone in a six-month time frame. Our six-month epic win would be that every Daybreak Church person would have invited someone to Daybreak Church." James was encouraged to see the staff nodding in approval. "Our hypothesis was that if we created a business card-size promo that explained the title of Pastor Tom's sermon series on hope from Nehemiah, along with service times, directions and a link to a 2-minute video, Daybreak Church folks would be more willing and able to invite their friends and colleagues to Daybreak Church. Our hypothesis was that the cards would create remove the friction and awkwardness of just inviting someone verbally, but the results were pretty minimal. Our people picked up only around 250 cards total and we've only heard a few stories on anyone that actually used one of them to invite someone."

So, what did your team learn, James?" asked Tom.

"Well, first of all, we probably shouldn't have started the whole idea with the cards after a sermon series is started. I think the promo needs to be planned out weeks before the series begins so we can get the value proposition right. Another thing we learned is that we might want to reserve the cards for events more than a church service. So, we may try the card for the Men's Fishing Retreat where men can invite their non-Christian friends. We are thinking about the tagline being, 'Hang out With Hookers?' We can work with something like that! So, our plan is to…pivot."

While the good-hearted laughter was dying down, Tom said, "Uh, yeah, 'Hang out with hookers'…um Okay. I guess this is the time to experiment." Tom advanced to the next slide. "What do you have around 'Keep,' Kai?"

Kaiya introduced her team and began. "Well, we wanted to solve for "Keep," which we defined as getting more first-time visitors to become regular attenders. The research showed that 60 percent of guests who attended three times made that church their home church. So, our hypothesis was that if guests attended three weeks in a row, that they could get a more coherent feeling of who we are and join with us in our mission. Our experiment was around extending an invitation each week to anyone who might be visiting, asking them to try us three-weeks in a row to get a feel of who we are and what we do. You know, like asking for the second date while still on the first date. The results were mixed. I made the announcement at the beginning of the service as part of the welcome and Pastor Tom did a good job ending the service with the same invitation, but we didn't see an increase in guests. So, what we learned was that summer is a lousy time to ask guests to attend three weeks in a row since June and July are historically our lowest attending months. A September start would have been better. That's when believers who have moved to town are putting their kids in school and actively looking for a church. So, we think we are onto something but would like to put this on hold for now so we will pivot and try something else on this next Sprint."

"Thanks for using that term 'Sprint' Kaiya. That's exactly what these six-week blocks of work are called. You want to tell us more about Sprints, Kai?" asked Tom.

"Yeah, sure. Sprints come out of a project management methodology called 'Agile Methodology.' You can Google all that, but I think most of you know the concept already from *The Lean Startup* book. So, Sprints are just the short development cycles that focus on continuous improvement. So, for us Sprints are all about "What we can do in this time block (Sprint cycle) to make progress towards our 'epic win?' All Sprint work is in service to accomplishing this epic win. So, Sprint methodology is designed to make us smarter and wiser with each Sprint cycle. Through 'validated learning' we see what's working and not working towards our epic win. The results we get tell us whether we should persevere or pivot."

"Oh, that's great," said Tom. "Yep, that's what we are doing...Sprints." Advancing to the next slide Tom said, "Okay, you're up Jerome with 'Grow.'

"We are solving for 'Grow.' How do believers become disciples? Our six-month epic win would be that every person at Daybreak Church would be on a satisfying growth journey and would be eager to recommend Daybreak Church to their friends and colleagues. From the data we developed a hypothesis that the key factor in being satisfied on their spiritual journey and the desire to recommend Daybreak Church to others was small group involvement. So, for our experiment the three of us challenged five people in our sphere of ministry, who had never been in a small group, to join a four-week small group around the first four chapters of the Gospel of John. We took a two-question assessment before we began and the same assessment afterwards. And we got great results. All fifteen participants went from not being satisfied with their spiritual progress to being satisfied. And, this is the exciting part, all of them went from net detractors to net promoters. So, we learned some good things. First, most people, if asked personally, will become part of a small group. We asked twenty-two people and fifteen of them said 'yes' and attended all four weeks. A second thing we learned is that small group involvement seems to be a critical factor in growth and willingness to recommend Daybreak Church to their friends and colleagues. So, we are going to persevere in getting more people involved in small groups. We loved this Sprint!"

"Very well done!" affirmed Tom. Jerome was beaming.

The lovefest was broken up when Dan, the Executive Pastor, spoke up. "That was good Jerome and team but have any of you heard of the Hawthorne Lighting Experiment?" His question was met with blank looks or shaking of heads. "Well, it was an experiment done at the Hawthorne plant of the Western Electric Company in Illinois in the late 1920s. The plant employed 45,000 workers and produced telephone equipment and consumer products like electric fans. Well, researchers wondered if increasing the lighting in the factory complex would increase productivity of the workers and sure enough, after increasing the factory lighting, productivity went up. Pretty simple. But then they wondered what would happen if they reduced the lighting in the factory and lo and behold, productivity went up again. What they took five years to discover was that it wasn't any specific environmental factor that increased productivity but the fact that the workers were being paid attention to and treated like they were important to the researchers. These factors are called 'confounding variables' and I just want to make the suggestion that it may not be the actual small group Bible study that brought about this significant change but maybe it was the fact that an admired church staff took interest in this congregant. We're starting to say around here, that 'relationships catalyze growth' not 'content catalyzes growth.' Just saying, keep an eye out for confounding variables."

Dan's comments, though correct, were probably not timely and took a bit of wind out of the sail as Tom was about to present his findings. "Thanks for setting me up," Tom said, trying to be lighthearted. "So, let me introduce my team." Tom began, "The problem we are solving is how we can help every Daybreak participant multiply the mission of our church. Currently around 40 percent of our people are contributing to fulfilling the mission of Daybreak Church through giving over $500 a year, leading a small group or church ministry, serving through one of our ministries, inside or outside the church, inviting their neighbors, evangelizing or discipling someone. Sixty percent are still just consumers of our mission. Our six-month epic win would be to have 100 percent of our people actually contributing to the advancement of the mission of the church. Our hypothesis is that over time, people are more satisfied through what they contribute than what they consume, so the more people we help get on mission, the healthier they and we as a church will be. So, our experiment was, at the end of my sermons, to create weekly opportunities to say 'yes' to one of these contributing activities. So, each week for the past six weeks I've ended my time on the podium with a specific call to action giving a vision for what would be possible in the areas of giving, serving, leading, etc. and the first clear step our folks could take. So, one week I ended my sermon by talking about automated giving, another week about serving in our food drive, another week about training for small group leaders, last week it was about becoming a host for National Night Out. So, we measured the results through the responses sent back via text messages. The results over the past six weeks have been encouraging. We've moved from 40 percent contributing to the mission to 48 percent contributing to the mission of the church. We learned that there is enough diversity in our people that one size does not fit all. We have to provide specific, often time-bound opportunities to contribute to the mission. The better we know our people the better we can match them to their place of contribution. So, we will persevere. Let's give it up for all the hard work you have done on your first Sprint."

Tom's cheerleading was followed by a raucous round of clapping and cheers. "We'll take a week off but at next week's all-hands meetings we'll be filling out our templates for our second Sprint—our six-week plan to get to our epic wins. So even if, in your report out you wanted to persevere, I want each team to go back to the Three-Minute Survey, study the data that Tanika gave us and start on a fresh problem to solve." Tom's assistant Marlene passed the templates around to the team leaders.

Experiment #2		Date: __/__/____
What problem are you solving for? (Attract, Get, Keep, Grow or Multiply?) Write a concise statement of the problem you are trying to solve:	Hypothesis #2: "We believe if we do _____ _____ _____ _____ it will lead to more of / less of _____ _____ (our desired outcome)"	Experiment #2 What you will do: Who will lead it: How you will measure it:
What would an "Epic Win" look like?	Notes:	What does "success" look like?

"Okay, let's talk a bit about National Night Out. I'm asking each of you and each of the elders to be the host of your block party. People are used to coming to a neighbor's National Night Out so it won't be weird. It's a neighborhood block party where people bring food and drinks and the police and fire department come by and visit. It'll be great. We'd add nearly twenty-five church locations if we join the twenty folks from the congregation who have signed up. It's a great way to let our light shine." The staff who hadn't already registered did so before the day was over.

At the elder meeting

Tom found it hard to believe that the past four weeks had flown by so quickly and it was time for the dreaded monthly elder meeting, on the last Tuesday of the month. A knot in Tom's stomach tightened as he prepared for his part of the meeting. Harold had been scribbling notes during Tom's sermons and had been eager to take Tom to task after each of his messages. Tom couldn't imagine what he'd bring up this meeting. He couldn't quite figure out why Harold was so adamant about getting rid of him. Sometimes he would wake up at three in the morning with his monkey brain running, trying to unravel what he had done to deserve being so unwanted as the pastor of Daybreak Church. He was about to find out.

After the reading and approval of June's elder meeting minutes, and a review of Daybreak's declining numbers, elder Sig Nelson gave a brief devotional—a reflection on

Tom's Sunday sermon on Nehemiah 9. Though Sig would regularly emphasize the importance of the Bible, he really wasn't a student of the Bible, so his devotionals were usually a rehash of what others had said, clichés or something he had read. "So, in conclusion I want to say that when we feel far from God, we should ask ourselves, 'Who moved?' Let us pray."

Tom felt a spark of encouragement from Sig's affirmation on his sermon so when asked to give his progress report, he did so with a renewed enthusiasm. "This last week we finished our first round of experiments to increase attendance, grow our people, and get more of our people active in our mission. And I wanted to share the results of what we did." Tom went on to briefly explain what each team was solving for, their hypotheses, the experiments they ran and the results they got. The elders listened intently looking to Harold to see how they should respond.

Harold measured his words. "Tom, we all appreciate the effort you've put in these past few months but to your own admission, forty percent of what you tried was a failure. When Pastor Arnie felt stuck, and there were many times when he felt stuck, he went to his knees in his prayer closet, he didn't pick up the latest business book. Our solutions are found in Christ alone. That's what this church was founded on, that's how we grew and that's how we'll grow and get back on track again. Your data is like your golden calf you're trusting in to take us out of Egypt."

Tom felt a surge of defensiveness but knew that any self-justification would be fruitless. "During this summer our verse as a staff is from 2 Chronicles 20:12 'Lord, we do not know what to do, but our eyes are on you.' So, our experiments are our best attempt to cast our bread upon the waters or to take our talents and invest them...not knowing exactly what we'll get. But we all want to advance the mission of God in this city."

"We're not going to constrain you, Tom. We've given you your full six months to improve but you only have two months left before we need to make a decision about your future here at Daybreak. And we are for you Tom. It's why we agreed to take you as our senior pastor last September."

Tom nodded, not in agreement nor acknowledgment but in concession.

Harold cleared his throat and began. "Yes, I want to introduce a guest this evening, well, more than a guest. I think all of you know him, my brother Ron Haynie. Ron and I both grew up in this church. Ron was discipled, as I was, by Pastor Arnie. Ron was a pastor for over twenty-years where he led a megachurch, more recently he was the CEO of a large Christian organization. At the same time, he has run different businesses and is known, in his circle, as a turn-around specialist. He was in town, so I've invited him to come, simply as an observer. Ron, do you have any observations from tonight's Board meeting?"

"Well, as you know, I'm a 30,000 feet guy so I would need more time to observe and gather information before commenting," said Ron. "But I heartily agree with my brother that the way forward will be found in digging deeper into God's word and I'm willing to help...if needed." The elders looked at each other and slowly nodded in approval. Tom felt his pulse increase as his muscles tensed.

"Well," said Harold, "we're so delighted that you're so willing to help at a time like this. And with your experience as a pastor...and the fact you grew up in this church...and have turned so many things around, I make the motion that we hire Ron as a consultant to take advantage of all he brings to the table. Do I have a second?"

One of the elders responded, "I second the motion."

"Any discussion?" asked Harold. "If not, all those in favor say 'aye.'"

The motion was passed. What the heck just happened? thought Tom.

As Tom drove into the underground garage, he found himself hoping that Amy would be home and still be up. As he entered the door Amy met him with a compassionate smile, "I've already poured the wine and have some cheese in the fridge. Now tell me about those buffoons that you call your elder board." Tom couldn't help but smile a bit.

"I could use one of those eight-second hugs right now," said Tom.

After a short hug, Amy looked at Tom to get his attention. "I know you might think that all that stuff about six-second kisses and eight-second hugs and our Saturday-night dates are improving our relationship Tom...but they are not." Tom waited for the other shoe to drop. But what Amy said surprised him. "What's helping us...what's helping me is not a technique or a new habit or something from the data. It's more how you bring me into your life now more than before. It's asking my opinion and thoughts. You initiate time with me and really want to know what's going on in my life. And you seek out my advice. I have no interest in being one of your data experiments, but I'm very interested in being your mate and companion and life-long lover."

Tom and Amy hugged and neither of them counted the seconds.

Friday, August 2. Colorado Rockies v. San Francisco Giants

Before leaving for Friday night's game against the Giants, Tom stuffed a couple of five-dollar bills into his left front pocket and began the short walk to Coors Field. There Francis was, strumming his guitar and singing the haunting, Johnny Cash song, "Hurt"...his last big record before he died. Tom moved in closer to Francis to listen to the lyrics...something about letting someone else having it all—the empire of dirt. Clapping, Tom walked up to the guitar case and put in a five-dollar bill. The look of recognition came over Francis' face and he smiled at Tom. "Hey thanks Dude."

"My name's Tom."

"Thanks Tom," said Francis. "Yeah, I remember you."
"I'm off to the game. Maybe I'll see you after the game,' said Tom.

"I'm not going anywhere," replied Francis.

The San Francisco Giants were in town for the first game of a three-game series. "Good to see you Bob," said Tom. "Boy a lot has happened in the past three weeks. This whole summer's been a roller coaster. So, what's up with the T-shirt Bob?"

Bob looked down at his chest.

"Oh! The ampersand. Did you know that little symbol used to be the 27th letter of our alphabet? It stands for the word 'and.' Just as the letter 'I' can mean the personal pronoun, 'I' or 'a' can also be the article 'a,' so the ampersand was the symbol for the word, 'and.' 'And' always connects one thing to another. It's the space in between. At Datanadec we created this T-shirt to help a company that was in a liminal place. I think this summer has been a liminal experience for you Tom," said Bob.

"What do you mean...'liminal?' I don't think I know that word," said Tom. "If so I'm all ears."

"Oh, liminal is a great concept and once I describe it, you'll get it and it will be a useful tool for your tool belt," teased Bob. "Liminality is the space between two different realities. It's that space between 'what used to work, but is no longer working' and 'what will work, but has not yet been revealed.' So, a liminal space would be the time when, in tribal societies, 13-year-old boys are wrested from their mothers, taken across the river, circumcised and then live with the men in a thatched hut for the next month. They are no longer boys, but they are not quite men. It's the time period when the Jews were taken into captivity and sitting by the rivers of Babylon trying to figure out how to connect with God in a foreign land. What used to work through their yearly calendar and physical temple was now gone. How would they connect with God in a foreign land?"

"So, it's like a transition space?" asked Tom.

"That's a good way to describe it," said Bob. "Liminality' is the space between two spaces. It's between a space you've left on the way to a space you're not yet fully in...maybe like a hallway or escalator."

"So, it's a place of uncertainty and ambiguity?" asked Tom.

"Yeah, the time between two epochs when what used to work no longer works but what will work has not yet been discovered." Bob pulled out one of his 3x5 cards and drew three "S" curves along with his definition.

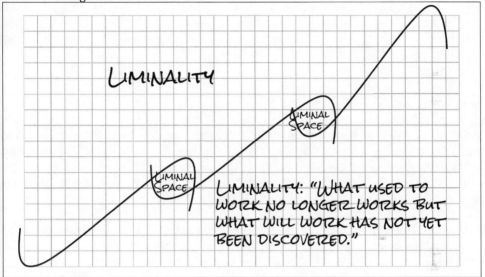

LIMINALITY

LIMINAL SPACE

LIMINAL SPACE

LIMINALITY: "WHAT USED TO WORK NO LONGER WORKS BUT WHAT WILL WORK HAS NOT YET BEEN DISCOVERED."

"Every living thing starts off growing slowly, then grows quickly before declining and dying. This is true with institutions, companies, churches and even people. So, that space between what was and what will be is the liminal space. There's always uncertainty, questioning and ambiguity. So enduring companies are always evolving, abandoning what used to work to embrace what will be useful in the future. This diagram probably describes the history of the church...from the founding to Constantine, from Constantine to the Reformation, the Reformation until today. About every 400 to 500 years there's been a major change. The old ways just don't work in the new realities and maybe we are on the brink of another reformation. In times of liminality, you might feel like a hermit crab running around the beach after abandoning the seashell you've outgrown. It's about abandoning what worked in the past to make room for the next thing."

"So, I think I get what you're saying about churches and institutions, but how does this work for people?" Tom asked.

Bob thought for a moment. "Look at the Apostle Paul. What did he say? 'When I was a child, I used to think as a child, speak like a child and reason like a child, but when I became a man, I put away childish things.' So, a belief and behavior system that worked wonderfully well for children doesn't work well for us as adults." And then tapping his pen on the second liminality space, Bob continued. "Then Paul added, 'For now we see in a mirror dimly but then we shall see face to face. Now we know in part, but then we shall know fully, just as we are fully known.' So here Paul talks twice about leaving behind old things in order to grasp onto the next thing God had for him. Seems that Paul was frequently forgetting what lies behind and reaching forward to what lies ahead. So, all growth involves leaving behind certain beliefs and behaviors that were true and useful at the time but need to be abandoned if one is going to embrace the next step God has for us. I've had to do that several times myself."

"This is all so new," said Tom. "But come to think about it...isn't that what Peter had to do in Acts 10 at the household of Cornelius?"

"Keep going," pressed Bob.

"Peter was so convinced that the gospel was just for the Jewish people...and maybe that conviction served him well when he was in Jerusalem. But as he went out into Judea, Samaria and the Mediterranean world, God needed to introduce him to a bigger, more inclusive reality that the Gentiles were always part of God's plan. He had to let go of one belief system in order to embrace a new belief system," said Tom.

"I think we should include this concept in our teaching and discipling...especially for our teens and new believers," said Bob. "I think a failure here is why so many young people are leaving the faith...when they are just leaving a version of the faith."

"What do you mean?" asked Tom.

"Well, we say things to our youth like, 'the same Bible that talks about a three-day resurrection also talks about a seven-day creation. They stand and fall together.' And so, for a while that works but then they go off to college where they learn the evidence for things like evolution and conclude that if a literal seven-day creation was not true, the resurrection isn't true either, and so they abandon Jesus, since these verses 'stand and fall together.'"

"Well, what would you say Bob?" asked Tom.

"To a new believer I might say something like, 'Here's a great way to get started. As you read your Bible, you need to do it with the attitude that 'God said it, I believe it and that settles it,' and take that as far as you can. But there could come a day when God is going to break your heart. Despite all your prayers, a loved one is going to die, the girl you love may break your heart and shatter your dreams; someone else will be on the victor's stand. That's not the time to abandon Jesus but to rediscover Jesus on the other side of your disillusionment.' So, growth is taking Jesus through every one of life's 'S' curves," said Bob.

"Man, that's a lot to think about," mused Tom.

The Rockies had a good night against the Giants, breaking a tie in the bottom of the seventh inning to go ahead 5 to 4, a lead they hung onto for the rest of the game. "I never knew what the time period between two innings was until tonight Bob," said Tom. "It's a liminal space, isn't it? And it's also the space where I've learned the most from you...in the space between two spaces. See you in a couple weeks against Miami?"

"Absolutely!" Bob affirmed. "Say hi to Amy for me."

"Say hello to Dana for me. Yeah, we still need to get together as the four of us," said Tom.

Liminality, Tom thought, walking home that night. Letting go of one thing in order to be ready for what comes next in order to keep growing. Spotting Francis, Tom crossed the street to hear him finishing his song, "Behind Blue Eyes," by Limp Bizkit. "To be mistreated...to be defeated...." Tom walked up to the guitar case and put the last of his five-dollar bills into the case, and looking into Francis' blue eyes said, "That was good Francis...that was really good."

"Thanks for saying that," said Francis. "It's been a tough week. I'm not used to living on the streets. You always got to have your guard up. I really want to get off the streets and get a job."

"When you're looking for work, what kind of work are you looking for?" asked Tom.

"'I've done a lot of graphics and web design and was getting an AA in Web Design and Development when my dad disowned me," Francis said. "I'm really good at it. I just need a chance."

"That must've really sucked," said Tom, a bit surprised at his own compassion. But it did feel good to have empathy towards another person. His world was becoming a little bigger and maybe his heart was growing a little softer.

"It's all chill," said Francis.

"Yeah, see you around," said Tom. And as he winded his way back home he found himself praying. "And thank you God for the grace to let go of old ways of thinking and acting that I might grasp the next thing you have for me. Give me new eyes and a new heart. And God, show me my part in helping Francis."

At home
"Looks like you had a good night," said Amy as Tom walked through the door.

"Yeah, I learned a new word tonight... 'liminality,' said Tom excitingly.

"Oh yeah, the space between the now and the not yet. Tell me all about it. Oh, and I found a great place for dinner for our date night tomorrow night. I'm so excited."

Tom wrapped his arms around Amy. "I'm so glad I married you. You're so dang smart... and kind of cute too. Now tell me about your day. Then we'll talk about me and my friend Francis. I've got a couple ideas."

Chapter twelve

At church

National Night Out wasn't a national holiday but it could have been. August is the only month of the calendar without a national holiday and National Night Out would be a good candidate to round out the calendar. Originally designed to promote understanding between communities and those who protect them, National Night Out had evolved into block parties complete with bands, organized games for kids and barbecues on the sidewalks. At a minimum there would be neighbors sharing a potluck barbecue on the front lawn of a neighbor. So many suburbanites knew few of their neighbors and so National Night Out filled a gap in the social fabric. Tom had read *The Art of Neighboring* and was on a mission to help the members of Daybreak become better neighbors. Hosting a block party on National Night Out was a logical first step. Loving ones' neighbor was just so basic.

At the Sunday morning service, those who hosted a National Night Out block party proudly wore a peel-and-stick red heart, signifying that they had hosted a block party and advanced Daybreaks' "Love Your Neighbor" initiative. Even Harold the elder and his wife June hosted a barbecue on their front lawn and determined that no alcoholic beverages be served on their property, so to be "family friendly," created a sign in front of the ice chest that simply said,

ALCOHOL

FREE

which neighbors took to mean, "Free Alcohol," so they soon replaced Harold's generic diet soft drinks with craft beers and white wine to be enjoyed by all. Soon a bar was set up around the ice chest and Tim, the most neighborly neighbor ever, served as bartender. Harold grilled hot dogs and hamburgers and as the saying goes, "A good time was had by all."

After Stephanie, the Director of Community Engagement, shared the impact of National Night Out, Tom got up to speak. "Knowing our neighbors is the first step to loving our neighbors. Whether you hosted a block party or just attended one; this was a great first step into loving our neighbors."

Tom's sermon on Nehemiah 10 was about the collection of tithes and first fruits concluding with a promise by God's people: "We will not neglect the house of our God." Tom went through the mission statement of the church along with examples of the expanding impact of the church. Tom thought this was a good time to help more people become contributors to the mission through their financial giving and encouraged people to become regular givers through automatic monthly bank transfers. Tom assured the congregants that they could regularly and automatically give online and if they did, it would be well worth it. Forty-six people who had never regularly given to Daybreak sent in a text message that would help move them from consumers to contributors. Tom was creating specific opportunities to say 'yes' to expanding the mission of Daybreak.

At church in the all-hands meeting
Tom stepped into the conference room for Monday's all-hands meeting to find the staff still buzzing over the success of National Night Out. "Let's get started, gang," said Tom. "Libby, I think you're up first."

"Thanks Pastor Tom," said Libby in her Arkansas accent. Libby was the energetic Director of Children's Ministry. "Y'all, I want to talk this morning about Mark 14:3-6 where Mary anoints Jesus' feet with perfume and the disciples get all upset because their scorecard was an economic scorecard. They are indignant over the waste of such precious resources. But Jesus was not operating from an economic scorecard but from a scorecard of beauty. 'What this woman has done is a beautiful thing' and we always need to leave room for beauty. After all, not everything that counts can be counted and not everything that can be counted really counts." She closed with a story about eleven-year-old Robbie, who played a beautiful song on the piano for his deaf mother who had passed away the morning of the recital. Libby had heard the story in a Sunday School Class on Mother's Day at her home church in Northwest Arkansas and wanted to work it into her devotional. It was a bit random, but the staff nodded in approval.

"Thanks Libby," said. "You guys are doing a great job on your Sprints and I thought this might be as good a time as any to pull back the kimono and show you the how's and why's behind your experiments. So, the big idea is that during times of uncertainty we don't have to know all the answers, we just need a process to make progress. Once you know what the goal is...what the 'win' looks like, there's no set way to start a data experiment. If we don't know what our 'win' is, there is no process that can help us. Having the endgame in mind is super important. The goal, or the win, ought to always be calling to you or at least be in the back of your mind all the time...if what we are trying to accomplish means anything to you personally. What are the big problems we are solving for at Daybreak Church? The more painfully specific we can be, the better. A problem well defined is a problem half-solved. How do we attract, get, keep, grow and multiply more at Daybreak? And how we start down that path can come from anywhere. We're more like 'decision scientists' than data scientists."

"Amen on that, Brother," said Juan.

Tom continued. "Sometimes we start from what's called the 'business question,' where we ask a specific question, like 'How might we double the number of weekly visitors?' or "How can we increase our giving by ten percent this year?" Or sometimes I'll start with data. So, a couple weeks ago I noticed we had seven people set up a monthly gift to Daybreak so that got me to ask the question, 'Do one-time gifts trigger long-time giving?' So, I think we could create a hypothesis and experiment to find out. Or I might see something someone else is doing in another area and wonder if we might be able to do something like that in church. So that got me thinking about doing some type of speed dating exercise at the new members class where people can get to know others rather than just listening to me ramble on about church distinctives. What can we learn from 'Go Fund Me' campaigns that we can apply to mission trips? Or, I think it's OK to start with a hunch."

"What do you mean, 'hunch?'" asked Dan, the Executive Pastor.

"Well, I've been thinking that maybe we are getting all the folks we can get on Sunday mornings. What if we started a 40-minute service on Thursday nights that include a kid's program for Coloradoans who are too busy on the weekends? As they say, 'If we want to reach people who no one else is reaching, we need to try things no one else is trying. My hunch is that it will work. It's asking, 'I wonder what would happen if...?'"

Dan nodded in approval.

"So, it really doesn't matter how we start...with a question, with data, with a hunch...whatever. It's the rigorous discipline of execution that follows."

"So, it's all about flexibility in how we begin but measured discipline in developing the hypothesis, experiment, measurement, decisive results and learning," said Tanika. "And then we either persevere or pivot."

"Exactly! That's a great way to put it, Tanika. And the better we get, the more progress we will make," said Tom. "We have God and tools to face the future and create the future. We build, we measure, we learn."

Tom ended the all-hands meeting with a group exercise called "I like / I wish." Each staff was given two post-it notes and asked to write down one thing they liked about the all-hands meeting and one thing they wished for going forward. One by one the staff walked up to the white board and pasted their sticky notes....

"I like the concept of starting anywhere...I wish we had taken the time to make it more practical."

"I like being with the staff each week...I wish we took time to talk about more personal things."

"I like that Tom brings us new information each week...I wish we could hear from some experts outside the church."

For the staff, the opportunity to give feedback was cathartic; for Tom, it was data to help determine what he'd do next staff meeting and who to follow-up with personally. Build, measure, learn.

Friday, August 16. Colorado Rockies v. Miami Marlins

The temperature was in the mid 80s at 20th and Blake Street as the former University of Oklahoma ace, Jon Gray, warmed up for the first inning of Rockies Baseball. The Miami Marlins had just trounced the 2018 National League champions, the L.A. Dodgers and were coming into Coors Field with a bluster of confidence. The stadium that provided the highest batting average in Major League Baseball was right here in the mile-high city.

After Tom sat down next to Bob, Tom reached up and gave a tug to the brim of his Astros ball cap. "I don't know if it's the sweat or because my head is getting fat, but I swear my Astros cap is shrinking. I used to wear it real tight over my eyes. Now it feels more like a beanie," said Tom as he sat down next to Bob.

"Well, you do have a choice, Tom," said Bob, adjusting his flat billed Rockies hat.

"That'll be the day. As the prophet Jeremiah said, "Can a leopard change…""

"Yeah, yeah, yeah," said Bob.

After standing for the National Anthem Bob and Tom took their seats. Both teams were tough defensively and by the end of two innings, with a near minimum of batters stepping to the plate, the score stood even at 0-0. "I had a good week with the staff. I think they're catching onto the idea of hypotheses and experimentation," said Tom.

"Yeah, and it's better if your staff do the work," said Bob.

"Well, that's what they say," said Tom. So, if that's true, what's my job then…I mean in your opinion?"

"I think of your job as the 'Chief Platform Architect' and that means you just have two responsibilities," said Bob.

"And those are?" asked Tom.

"First to motivate people to do what God wants done in this world and to provide tools to help them do it." Said Bob. "Another way to put this is 'decrease friction and increase fuel.'"

"Where'd that come from?" ask Tom with a bit of confusion.

"That was a bit unfair of me. It's just that since we met I've been thinking about church as a 'platform,'" said Bob.

"I have no idea what you're talking about Bob," said Tom.

"Well, I guess you need to know a bit about platforms for this to make sense. Is this a good time?" asked Bob.

Fourteen Fridays - 140

"As good as any," said Tom.

"Look at my T-shirt," said Bob.

Tom looked at the white letters on the black T-shirt, a bit overwhelmed by the verbiage.

"UBER, THE WORLD'S LARGEST TAXI COMPANY, OWNS NO VEHICLES. FACEBOOK, THE WORLD'S MOST POPULAR MEDIA OWNER, CREATES NO CONTENT. ALIBABA, THE MOST VALUABLE RETAILER, HAS NO INVENTORY. AIRBNB, THE WORLD'S LARGEST ACCOMMODATION PROVIDER, OWNS NO REAL ESTATE. SOMETHING INTERESTING IS HAPPENING." TOM GOODWIN

"Wow!" said Tom. "So, what determines if something can be a platform or not?" asked Tom.

"Well, that's what I've been asking myself lately," said Bob. "Here's what I've come up with. First, platforms take advantage of the energy around 'what wants to happen.' I think that's the best way to say it. So, for instance, people have always wanted to have a large selection of great products and sellers have always wanted to have a huge market of potential customers. Amazon simply brought these two parties together to exchange value. So, I think the latent energy of the church is found in Ephesians 2:10. Everyone is created to do something redemptive in the world—a 'good work' that God has prepared for them to do—these are the same things God wants for every person. The church acts as the platform to bring together what God wants and what people long to do, in the same way Amazon brings together buyers and sellers or Airbnb brings together hosts and guests or Uber connects riders and drivers."

"Okay, I think I see where you are going with this. So, the church facilitates what wants to happen. What else?" asked Tom.

"Well, every platform has what's called a 'core interaction'—a single action, that when done, advances the mission of the platform organization. So, if Uber's mission is to make transportation as common as running water, what do you think Uber's core interaction is?"

"Well, I think the success of their business is to connect riders with drivers and then actually completing the ride and paying the driver," said Tom.

"A little long, but that's right. How about Airbnb?" asked Bob.

"Having guests stay with hosts and paying the bill," said Tom.

"That'll do. There's a lot of other interactions people take like entering credit card information, checking a host's rating but the one core interaction, on which the future of the company depends, is room nights rented. Every other edge interaction serves that one

Fourteen Fridays - 141

core interaction. So, for you Tom, what do you think is the interaction that you're trying to do, repeat and scale to fulfill your God-given mission?"

Tom was stumped and stammered a bit, grasping to find the right words. "Ah...er...um, let me go get us something to drink and let me think about it a bit," said Tom.

"Yeah, it's sort of the question of the day, so give it some thought," said Bob smiling.

Now Tom was really stumped but he prayed for clarity as he walked up the stairs to the concession stand. I should have downloaded PrayerChimp. Let's see now.... Then the answer came to his mind as assuredly as an epiphany from God himself. But he'd need to test it with Bob.

Tom returned excitedly to his seat. Handing a Coors Light to Bob, Tom said, 'I think I've got the answer."

"Well, go on," said Bob.

"A few weeks ago, you told me that I could define my job in seven words: 'Attract, Get, Keep, Grow, Multiply, Know and Match.' I suspect you knew what you were talking about back then so I suspect the core interaction of any and every platform is...drumroll please...'Know and Match.' I think it is true for Amazon, Airbnb, Uber and Daybreak Church. How'd I do? Am I right?" asked Tom, looking for approval.

"Gosh, I think you've nailed it, Tom. Well done," said Bob. "Every platform's core interaction is about knowing and matching—knowing what I want as a consumer and matching me to a product or service from a provider or producer. Or knowing what I have to offer as a producer or provider and matching me to someone who is looking for that product or service. The core interaction is always about know and match."

"Well, thanks Bob. It's just so simple, isn't it?" commented Tom.

Bob continued. "So, we have what wants to happen and the core interaction. The third thing is about scaling the core interaction and how quickly you scale your core interaction. So, I can ride with Uber today and be driving for Uber tomorrow. I can stay in an Airbnb property today and list my house on Airbnb tomorrow. I can read something on Facebook and then create a like or a comment and so immediately become a creator. So how quickly can a new believer lead someone else to Christ? How quickly can those who are taught, teach someone else?"

Tom hesitated for a moment then answered Bob's rhetorical question. "Well...I think scaling is slower than just posting a comment or driving for Uber, but I do think the scaling is found in passages like 2Timothy 2. 'The things you have heard from me, entrust to faithful men who can teach others also.' That's four generations—Paul, Timothy, faithful men and others. Over time Paul got to know Timothy and matched him to the appropriate next steps. If Timothy repeated the process with faithful men, the process will go on."

"It *has* gone on. That's how the gospel has spread. It's called 'discipleship,'" said Bob.

"So true...so true," said Tom. So, what's the fourth thing every platform has?"

"That'd be tools," Bob said. Tools are designed to remove the friction to make the core interaction, repeatable, simple and common. So, think of all the barriers to getting into cars with strangers. It's why you rarely if ever see a hitchhiker anymore. So, Uber creates tools that remove the friction of driving with a stranger. You can see what the driver looks like, the make, model and license plate of the car. You can see the star rating of the driver and how many rides she has given. You can see what the ride will cost you before you step into the car. For every objection, Uber has created a tool to eliminate that objection."

"Wow, I hadn't thought of that," said Tom.

"So, one more thing about tools. Tools give ability to the willing but by themselves don't make the unwilling...willing. So, a good evangelism or discipleship tool will greatly increase the effectiveness of someone who wants to share Christ or disciple another, but by themselves are basically inert," said Bob.

"So, how did you describe my job...as the chief platform architect?" asked Tom.

"Yes, the chief platform architect with two jobs—to motivate people and then provide them with tools to follow through on the action you want them to take. So, if your core interaction is all about knowing your people and matching them to an action you want them to take, your team needs to find or create tools that makes that core interaction, simple, repeatable and common, whether it be reading the Bible, praying, sharing the gospel or inviting someone to church," said Bob.

"I think I get it," said Tom. "So, if I wanted to turn non-givers to givers, I'd need to give them a simple tool. And I don't have to create what I can curate."

"That's right," said Bob. "So, for one-time gifts, a great tool is text GIVE to such-and-such number. If you want to encourage a monthly gift, give them a tool that creates a monthly auto-transfer. Your rule of thumb ought to be to never ask someone to take a conversion step without giving them a tool that helps them do it. It's like the guy in the Bible who asks, 'What must I do to be saved?' Paul gave him an answer that he could apply right then and there."

"This makes so much sense. I need to write this down. Uh, can I have one of those cards Bob?" Tom wrote:

```
Platforms
1. Based on "What wants to happen"
2. The "core interaction"—know and match
3. Scaling the core interaction
4. Tools that make the core interaction
   simple, repeatable and common
(I'm the Chief Platform Architect:
I motivate others and I provide tools)
```

Going into the bottom of the sixth inning Rockies' pitcher, Jon Gray was on fire. He had just finished his fourth consecutive inning of three-up, three-down baseball and the Rockies hung onto a 2-0 lead. Tom thought it might be a good opportunity to ask Bob about something that he found himself thinking about lately. "Hey Bob, what do you do to develop the people in your company? Or what did you do at your last company? As I've been giving staff more leadership opportunities, I think I need to be more intentional about developing my staff," asked Tom.

"That's a good question," Bob said. "I think there are a lot of good training and developmental tools out there, but I think a person's job...especially challenging work itself is a great developmental tool if they are taking their job seriously and have some big, significant objectives they are trying to accomplish."

"So, what do you do, specifically to help them grow?" asked Tom.

"Once they understand their assignment I just check in every week and ask three questions," said Bob.

"And those are...?" Tom asked with anticipation.

"First, 'How's it going?' The body language will tell you a lot. Then, 'Where are you winning this week?' This gives them a little time to brag about their work or their team. Then we talk about the biggest problem or challenge they are facing. And I just let them talk. Then...and this is super important, I ask, 'What are you going to do about it?' That's it."

"Well, where do you offer to help?" asked Tom.

"I don't. When I entered that person's space, if that person has a work problem, there was a monkey on his or her back. I want to be sure that when I leave, that monkey's not on my back. Problem solving is what leaders do. Why would I take that developmental process away?" Bob asked with a smile. "And I'm intentional about giving work assignments which are difficult but do-able...enough to grow and stretch them but not break or discourage them. I learned a lot from this guy, whose last name I can't pronounce...Mihaly Cheek-something-or-other. But here's his diagram." Bob pulled out another card and began to draw.

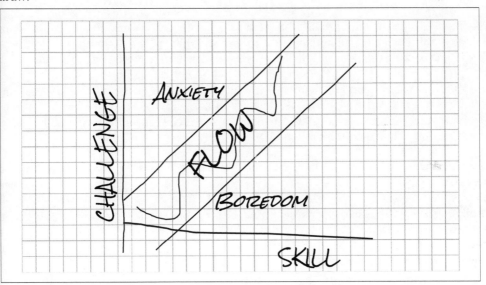

People grow in what he calls the 'Flow' state. When skills are greater than the challenge, we get boredom. If we get challenges greater than our skills, we get anxiety, so we need to keep our challenges in the flow channel. So, after a while things which were quite challenging now become quite easy. Individual competency and team competency grow through this flow channel."

"Don't you have any standing appointments with people," asked Tom.

"No, I have office hours every week where anyone can schedule a 20-minute appointment with me. That's where they usually ask me for advice or counsel. Before they leave, I always give them an assignment...to read an article...watch a TED talk...buy a book...something like that to help them solve their problem. Then I tell them to set up another appointment when they have completed their assignment. And I've found that only one or two out of ten take me up on my suggestion and follow through with their assignment. So, all the people who I meet with a second time and beyond are growing and

Fourteen Fridays - 145

making real progress in their lives," said Bob. "By the way Tom, you're one of those folks I love meeting with. Whenever I give you a suggestion, you write it down and implement it."

"Thanks Bob. I should do something like that with my staff," said Tom.

In the bottom of the eighth inning Rockies' Nolan Arenado knocked one out of the park ensuring a 96 percent possibility of walking away with a win. The Rockies ended the game shutting out the Marlins, 3-0. The game lasted a mere two hours and 12 minutes. The night was still young.

As they were getting out of their seats Tom said, "I talked with Amy about the four of us taking in the last Friday night game next month and then hanging out afterwards. Check with Dana to see if that works. It'll be a great way to celebrate our last game together."

"Sounds like a plan," said Bob handing Tom the card with the Flow Diagram. "By the way, I think this is the way God grows us. He gives us assignments to stretch us and keep us dependent on him, so our normal state is to always feel a bit off balance and unsure of ourselves and out of our comfort zone."

Well, that would explain a lot of things, thought Tom. "Thanks Bob. See you in a couple weeks."

Walking home as Tom crossed Market Street, he spotted a familiar face and Francis began to sing.

"Hello Darkness, my old friend…"

It was an old Simon and Garfunkel song and Tom moved in closer. He hadn't heard that one in a while and Francis had a classic troubadour's voice that was especially soulful tonight. When Francis finished, Tom clapped as he stepped forward to put a five spot into the guitar case. "Well done, Francis," Tom said. "You know a lot of old tunes."

Francis smiled. "Yeah, I grew up listening to my dad's old albums. And some songs I just can't get out of my head," said Francis.

The crowd that passed by Francis and Tom got increasingly thinner as people found their way to restaurants, bars or their cars. A street entertainer was nothing more than part of the background soundtrack on a warm summer night in the city. Francis looked into his guitar case and gathered up the bills and change, about thirty dollars in all. "I was thinking about getting a couple Tacos down at G's," said Tom. "You hungry?"

"If you're treating, I'm hungry," replied Francis with surprise. "You really want to buy me dinner?"

"Why not?" said Tom and they walked down the block toward G's Tacos where Tom requested patio seating. When the chips and salsa arrived, Tom realized they'd both be putting their hands into the same basket of chips. Who knows where Francis' hands have been today? "Chips are all yours Francis. I'm trying to lose a few pounds, so I think I'll just stick with the Cowboy Burrito. How long have you been playing and singing?"

"Probably since middle school. I was part of the worship team at my church," Francis answered nonchalantly.

Tom almost choked on his burrito but collected himself and asked calmly, "So, tell me about that, ah your church experience and all."

"Oh, I was really into it. I played guitar and sang on the worship team. I did all the graphic and web design for the church since I was fifteen. I mean for some reason I discovered what makes websites work or not. Well, I even thought I might go into ministry, it was so much fun, but I also knew I was different...you know, being gay and all. I tried to be straight and thought and prayed I'd outgrow my feelings towards other guys and I even had a girlfriend in High School. Looking back, it's kind of funny that I was always pointed to as the example of a 'godly young man' who was content to simply hold a girl's hand and not try anything," said Francis with a smile.

"So, what happened then?" asked Tom.

"My senior year I just had to tell someone, so I told my youth pastor that I thought I was gay. That's when the circus and sideshow began. Word got around really fast in the church. Now, I hadn't actually done anything at this point, just some online porn maybe but had never actually done anything. Soon I was at this PGA intensive...oh...Pray the Gay Away intensive and I was on my knees and people were praying Scripture over me. And I wanted to be cured, I wanted to change and when the intensive was over, by faith I pronounced that I was no longer a homosexual and that God had healed me. Then after that I was sort of a hero at church and spoke at different churches around town. But as much as I wanted this to be true, I knew in my heart I was still gay, but I kept that to myself. I eventually amended my story to say the temptation was still there, but God had given me the gift of celibacy. More than once I thought of killing myself."

Tom just listened. If his Texas friends could see him now. But strangely that didn't mean anything to him at this moment.

"When I started college, I met Travis and we started hanging out. I just did not want to be alone and be celibate my whole life. I just didn't, so when Travis and I moved in together, in the Spring, that's when it really hit the fan. My dad went crazy. I think he felt my sexuality was somehow his fault but that's what they taught at my church...about having a dominant mother and a weak father. That's when he kicked me out of the family and Travis and I moved out here." Francis dabbed a tear from under his eye. "I suppose you didn't want to hear all of that," said Francis. "I'm sorry man."

"No, I've just never really had a conversation like this before. You're really helping me. Can I ask you where you are now in your relationship with God?" asked Tom.

"I'm not even sure I believe in God anymore...but I sure miss him," said Francis.

Tom didn't have any answers, though he wished with all his heart that he did. "You're a good person, Francis. Never forget that. And you are deeply loved and valued by God." Tom paid the tab. "Where will you be staying tonight?"

"I've got a tent in Triangle Park by Samaritan's House. It's working out okay. Thanks for asking."

Tom walked home, consciously grateful he had a home...and a good person to come home to. He enjoyed so much of the goodness of God. "God, help Francis and God please help me."

At home
"You won't believe the conversation I had tonight Amy," said Tom thoughtfully as he stepped through the door.

"I'm all ears," said Amy getting off the couch and moving toward Tom. "Let me grab a couple glasses and you can tell me all about it."

Tom opened up. "It's kind of frightening to think how 'right' I might feel about something, but how wrong I really might be...and the way I've been so judgmental and self-righteous," said Tom. "Sometimes I feel like I haven't grown at all. I've got better skills and some pastoral habits but has my heart really been changed in the past thirty years?"

"You're on a good path Tom. We're on a good path Tom. Maybe this is why God brought us to Denver...to give us bigger hearts and bigger, more embracing arms."

"That would be worth it...yeah, that would be worth it."

Chapter thirteen

At church

Tom looked over the crowd in the first service and was happy to see that the summer slump was over. Tom wished he had better material to speak from. Nehemiah 11 was about the repatriation of Jerusalem, the kind of material the Bible Sleep App was designed for. Tom felt it was a good time to talk about what God wants in every city and cross-referenced Isaiah 65:17-25, the passage about the New Jerusalem. "When God builds a city from scratch what does he include? What's an ideal city look like?" he asked rhetorically. "It's a place of health where people live long lives and no children die. It's a place where there is abundant food, housing and meaningful work, where people are 'satisfied by the work of their hands.' There is intergenerational family support where the family structure is intact. People are connected to God, seeing rapid answers to prayer and 'the wolf lies down with the lamb'—there is reconciliation and an absence of violence." Tom closed by presenting three options for living in the city where God placed us. "Culture is like boiling water. You put an egg in boiling water, and the egg gets harder. You put a potato in boiling water, and the potato gets softer. But you put salt into boiling water and it's the water that is changed and becomes salty. God has called us to be the salt of our community and we have a great opportunity to make a difference in Denver."

Overall, Tom thought the message had gone well until Harold confronted him in the foyer for preaching "such a message from the left." He accused Tom of being a socialist. "'It is the wise man's heart that leads him to the right and the foolish man's heart that leads him to the left.' Ecclesiastes 10:2," said Harold as he walked off. Tom didn't change a thing about his message in the second service.

At church at the all-hands meeting

Tom looked forward to the all-hands meeting on Monday morning. He had a growing affection for the staff and any wind taken out of his sail at the dreaded elder meetings was being replenished at the all-hands meeting on Monday mornings. "I believe you're up this morning Lonnie. By the way, the bathrooms were sparkling this morning. Thanks for all you do around here."

"Thanks Pastor Tom. I have a good crew and thanks for giving me this opportunity. And I want you all to know how much I love working here at the church. Last month I came across the passages where Jesus said what he had come for...those passages that say, 'The Son of man came...' and I found three of them. 'The Son of Man came to seek and save the lost...The Son of Man came not to be served but to serve' and 'The Son of Man came eating and drinking.'" A small chuckle rippled through the room. "So that's what the data said. So, then I went to analytics...what does that mean? I think it means that the way Jesus went about reaching lost people was to serve them and by eating and drinking with them. So, my hypothesis was that if Maria and I served our neighbors by having them to dinner, we may see some of them come to faith. So, our experiment was last Saturday night when we hosted a *carne asada* dinner for four of our neighbors and their kids. Maria cooked. I made *Horchata*, someone brought a *piñata* for the kids. We ended the time by circling up, holding hands and I said, 'Does anybody need any prayer?' That works for us in our culture. And we ended up praying for Oscar and Maya's son in Afghanistan. And they were the ones that asked if they could come to church with us yesterday and they loved your message, so we are going to persevere with our monthly dinners."

"I have his visitor's card right here, said Jerome. He says he wants more information on how to become a Christian."

"*Gracias a Dios*," said Lonnie, wiping a tear from his eye.

"Thank you, Lonnie for such a good word," said Tom. "I know that some of you have been asking to get some time with me and I want to be with you so I'd like to set up some office hours where any of you can get a concentrated 30 minutes with me to ask me anything, personal, ministry, your career, your ministry track...whatever. So, I'll start with Tuesdays and Thursdays 2-4pm. Marlene's created a Google doc where you can sign up if you're interested. It's my experiment in staff development."

At the elder meeting
Tuesday evening came too soon for Tom. His two office hours that day filled up immediately and he had left each of the staff with an assignment to complete before their next appointment. I think we'll really make some progress this way, he thought.

But now God had prepared a table for him in the presence of his enemies. And he thought that each of the elders was an enemy. He learned in seminary that an enemy was anyone who opposed what you were trying to get done, but Jesus told us to love our enemies so in the end he'd be civil and try to be loving.

After the call to order, reading and approval of the July minutes, Harold turned to elder Jim Keyworth. Jim was a locksmith and a very good locksmith, Tom had heard. But he probably shouldn't be on the ruling board of a large church. Jim served as Harold's wingman fetching coffee for Harold and was there with a fresh dry-erase marker when Harold was writing on the white board. If Harold said it, Jim believed it and that settled it. Jim's passage was on the replacement of Judas from Acts 1. "We all sincerely hope that Pastor Tom continues on as our pastor at Daybreak..." The B.S. detector in Tom's brain flashed a hot red. "But if he should need to be replaced, the Scripture says it should be someone 'who has been with us from the beginning.' I think it's no coincidence that Ron has been with us this last month. He grew up here, was trained by Pastor Arnie and when the time comes, I'd like to put forth a motion that we call Ron as our next pastor." Tom winced as his stomach churned.

Harold gave Jim a faux look of reproach. "We're too premature in the process, Jim, to decide on our next pastor but you've made an excellent suggestion and it is good to plan ahead. We still have one month to make our decision."

Decision my ass, Tom fumed. The decision's been made. Jim Keyworth was Harold's pawn. I don't know who Ron has been talking to in his turn-around effort. He's never once given me a call. I just wish I knew what I was going to do. God help me.

At home
Tom walked into the apartment a bit before nine. How his spirits were lifted when Amy handed him a cold copper cup. "Moscow Mules," she said. "Now, speaking of mules, come and tell me all about the elder meeting those jackass elders of yours."

"I'm sure they are good people," Tom started.

"Oh, cut the B.S. Tom. If you can't be real with me, who else do you have?" asked Amy.

Tom smiled. "Okay let me tell you about those jackasses." It felt good to be loved. It felt good to be cared for and to have one person in your corner to come home to. Pity anyone who falls and has no one to pick him up, he thought and couldn't help but think about Francis, alone on the streets of Denver.

Friday, August 30. Colorado Rockies v. Pittsburgh Pirates
The Pittsburgh Pirates shared a nearly identical Won-Loss record as the Rockies when they beat the Rockies 11-8 on Thursday evening. But that was yesterday. Tom found his way to his seat and Bob joined him shortly thereafter. "I'm thirsty from just walking over here," said Tom. "And the burrito guy was sold out of steak and potato, so I didn't even grab a water. Proverbs says, 'Give beer to him who is perishing,' and right now I'm *dying* of thirst. I'm going for a beer. You want one?"

"Ah, yeah and grab a couple peanuts," Bob said, handing Tom a ten spot.

As Tom sat down, Bob turned to him, grabbed his Coors Light and said, "Well you've got a big month ahead of you. You feel okay about it?"

"Well as much as I'd like to stay, I'm mentally resigned to the fact I'll be gone in a month," said Tom. "And you and I only have a couple more games together. So, I thought I better get what I can from our time together. Maybe I'll learn something I can take into my next job. Do you mind if I ask a few questions?"

"Hey, that's why I'm here," said Bob, turning his upper torso towards Tom. There was his T-shirt proclaiming,

"EVERYTHING IS OBVIOUS ONCE YOU KNOW THE ANSWER." DUNCAN J. WATTS

Tom smiled. "So, here's my first question. When we first met, you told me about All God's Kids Got Mojo. You said my job could be boiled down in seven words—Attract, Get, Keep, Grow and Multiply and then Know and Match. And I've found that to be incredibly helpful in keeping my eye on the ball. I've got your card taped over my desk to keep me focused.

So that's my job...that's what I've got to figure out. But for the people in the city and the people in my church, I don't think they stay awake thinking, 'How can we help Tom be successful in *his* job?' They are thinking about what they are trying to get done. Have you given any thought to why a person would be attracted to our church, visit our church, stay, grow and multiply our mission?"

"That's a profound and insightful question Tom. But just as you have a job to do that makes you successful, each person in Denver and in your church has a job to be done and your success will come as you match your job to their job," said Bob.

"Keep going," encouraged Tom.

"A few years ago, an article came out in the *Harvard Business Review* called 'Know Your Customers' Jobs to be Done,' something like that. The big idea was whenever a customer purchases something they are 'hiring' that product to do a job for them. So, a 'job' is shorthand for what an individual really wants in a given situation that goes beyond the features of the product or service. So, Starbucks may think they sell coffee so if sales start to slip, they might form focus groups to discover how they might improve their coffee or create a better variety of breakfast foods or salads. I went to Starbucks three times today and each time I 'hired' them for three different reasons. At seven o'clock this morning I hired a cup of black coffee to get my day started. At 10 o'clock I went back and bought two more cups of coffee and a couple of scones for a meeting with one of my old friends who was in town. I didn't really need another cup of coffee to get my day started. The job I needed done at ten this morning was to have a comfortable place to sit and talk with an old friend. I hired the coffee to pay my rent, that gave us permission to sit there for that hour. I went back to Starbucks at four to pick up a Frappuccino for my assistant after a tough day. This time I hired a cup of coffee as a way of saying, 'Thanks...you matter.' Same basic coffee but I hired that coffee for three different jobs I needed done. Sometimes I hire a 20 oz cup of coffee to keep me company when I'm driving down to Colorado Springs. Sure, I like the coffee, but I like a little something to do while I drive even if it is just pulling the coffee cup from the cup holder. Maybe it's similar to the old saying, 'People don't want a quarter inch drill bit. They want a quarter inch hole.' So, when Proctor and Gamble discovered that millions of people without cold symptoms were hiring NyQuil to help them sleep, they created ZzzQuil and sales of ZzzQuil soared—and is now the number one sleep aid with sales somewhere in the neighborhood of $80 million last year."

"Wow, that's a fascinating concept...jobs to be done," said Tom. "So that explains why some couples drop their kids off at Sunday School and skip the service and go out to breakfast. They've hired the church to give them some time together as a couple."

"You got it. Even here at the game. The Rockies may think that people are here to watch them play but I think there are a thousand jobs being done here tonight. I mean...well, look up in the luxury boxes. The owners of those boxes hired the Rockies to impress their clients. And look at that dad over there with the two small boys with their baseball mitts. Maybe he hired the Rockies to give his kids a love of the game. I mean jobs to be done applies to so many areas of our lives...the cars we drive...the clothes we wear." Bob looked up at Tom's Astros ball cap. "What are you hiring that under-sized, ratty-old Astros cap to do today? Certainly not to keep your head warm on a day like today."

"I guess I hired this cap to keep the sun out of my eyes or maybe to tell the world I'm proud to be an Astros fan," said Tom.

"Okay, I think you're getting the concept of jobs to be done," said Bob. "So, let's talk about how this applies to the Church Engagement Framework." Bob pulled out a card and started drawing. "While your job is to Attract, Get, Keep, Grow and Multiply, what's their journey like? I think in the gap there are always four stages a person goes through before they go on to the next stage. They become *aware* of a new possibility, they *consider* that next step, they *evaluate* the pros and cons, costs and benefits and then they *commit*...or don't commit and stay where they are. If you want to do your job well, you have to help them do *their* job well."

Bob continued writing. "Everyone goes through this same growth and impact journey. They become aware of an opportunity, they consider it and evaluate it before ever committing to that next step. They are thinking, 'I want to know more' or 'I want to try it out,' or 'I want to stay,' or 'grow' or 'contribute.' That's the journey they are on. And, by the way, there's almost always a trusted person in the gap that helps them take that next step...who catalyzes their growth. So, although your job is 'know and match,' their job is to 'know and trust' before they take that next step. Trust is the most important currency that keeps people on their engagement journey. The more trust, the more people who make progress in their growth-impact journey."

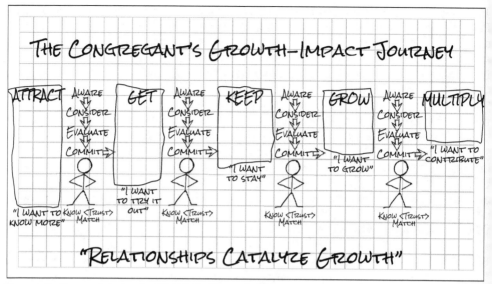

THE CONGREGANT'S GROWTH-IMPACT JOURNEY

ATTRACT — GET — KEEP — GROW — MULTIPLY

AWARE → CONSIDER → EVALUATE → COMMIT

"I WANT TO KNOW MORE" — KNOW <TRUST> MATCH

"I WANT TO TRY IT OUT" — KNOW <TRUST> MATCH

"I WANT TO STAY" — KNOW <TRUST> MATCH

"I WANT TO GROW" — KNOW <TRUST> MATCH

"I WANT TO CONTRIBUTE"

"RELATIONSHIPS CATALYZE GROWTH"

"So, part of your job as the Chief Platform Architect is to provide tools that reduce the friction along their journey that makes it easy and likely to go from Attract to Get, Get to Keep, to Grow, etc. Make it easy for them to want to check you out, stay, grow and contribute by removing their uncertainty...giving them a vision and hope to help them take that next step," Bob said.

"I never thought of this from a congregant's point of view," said Tom. "I must've been living in a cave or something."

Bob continued. "So, getting back to their jobs to be done, ask yourself, 'What are they hiring your church to do if they come, stay, grow and contribute? The better you help them with their job to be done, the easier it will be for you to do your job. You may find a lot of surprises along the way. It takes us back to that question, 'How can you and your church be a tactic in their strategy?' How can you help them win?"

Tom took the card out of Bob's hand. "Thanks Bob, you have a great way of explaining this."

"Oh, any ten-year-old boy could do what I just did," said Bob who was quick to add, "with 30 years of practice of course."

Bob and Tom settled down to watch the game. Tom scanned the fans imagining what each one might be hiring the Rockies to do that evening. So many delicious possibilities. And here I thought the people in my church hired the church because of my preaching, he thought and smiled.

The Pirates led off strong, scoring first and scoring often. By the bottom of the fifth, the Pirates held a commanding lead, 5-1 and Tom had another question. "So, you've given me so many good ideas Bob, but my experience at my other church was that as much as people say they want change, they really resist change and if I can't get at least 51 percent buy-in, I really don't have a mandate to lead that change."

"Well, that's one way of looking at it," said Bob. "But if I can be honest, it's the wrong way to look at it."

"If there's another way, I'm all ears," said Tom.

Bob reached into his pocket and pulled out a 3x5 card and started drawing. "Back in the 1960s this guy named Everett Rogers started researching how new ideas were adopted.

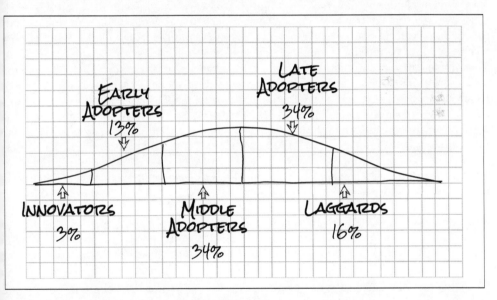

Bob started filling in his bell-curve diagram. "So, Rogers said that about 3 percent of people are innovators. They see things in new ways. They are creative and inventive. They are idea people. Then there's another 13 percent...the Early Adopters who, when they hear the idea say, 'we can do that' or 'I'm buying one.' It doesn't matter to them if anyone else is doing it or even if all the bugs are out of the product, they just love being first. They are happy to be involved in something new and innovative. The next group, the Middle Adopters ask a different question. They ask, 'Does this thing actually work?' and that must be answered before they jump on board. The next 34 percent are the Late Adopters. They want to know, not only if this new product or idea works but if this new thing works in their setting...for people like them. And then come the Laggards. The Laggards make up around 16 percent and they are the last to get on board or never get on board...and often serve on church boards. In the Bible, they would be the ones who said, 'The old wine is good enough.' And, by the way, these are not personality types so you can be an early adopter in one area of your life but a laggard in another area."

"Yeah, I was just going to ask about that," said Tom.

"So, here's the big idea. Whenever you introduce a new idea...a new way of doing things...any change initiative in your church, don't vote on it, just start with the willing...that 13 to16 percent of people who respond to the new thing. And then put them up in front of your congregation and have them tell their story of how the new thing is affecting their lives. You don't argue with the Laggards. You just start with the willing and feed the new and starve out the old."

"What do you mean, 'feed the new' and 'starve the old?' asked Tom.

"I remember when my dad was working towards each small group having a missional focus by partnering with a local human service agency and then serving with them six or eight times a year in place of meeting to study the Scriptures that week. So, it really took no more time to be missional than it did to sit at someone's house eating chips and dip. At first only ten or so groups jumped on board, so he worked with them and helped them tell their story from the front of the church. That was the new norm. And, over the course of about 18 months nearly every small group had a missional focus and it changed the whole vibe of the church. He'd often ask, 'What should be different in the world because your small group meets...what evil should die...what good should thrive?'" said Bob. "Feed the new. Starve the old."

"I really like this concept Bob. So, I don't need a majority of folks to get on board...I just need to start working with the willing," said Tom.

"I suppose I have a moral obligation to read you the warning label," said Bob soberly.

"Huh?"

"This diagram can also work backwards. If the Laggards are the people in power, the innovators and early adopters, who introduce change initiatives are either marginalized, if they are lay people or fired if they are staff," Bob said.

"Oh crap!" said Tom. "I don't think I'd classify any of the elders as 'innovators' or 'early adopters.'"

"Just keep working with the willing...like your staff," advised Bob.

At the bottom of the fifth inning, Rockies' second baseman Ryan McMahon's single was enough to get Trevor Story across home plate. Pirates 6, Rockies 2. "I'm really happy to see McMahon having such a good season," said Bob.
"I don't know that much about him," said Tom.

"He's from Mater Dei High School in Southern California and was on his way to play ball for USC when the Rockies drafted him back in 2013 and McMahon started off playing for the Grand Junction Rockies, the Ashville Tourist, the Modesto Nuts, the Hartford Yard Goat and the Albuquerque Isotopes before being called up by Rockies in 2017. But then last year he was sent back to the Isotopes. Those minor league teams are a grind...a lot of bus rides. But this year he's coming into his own both on defense and offense. He's batting a respectable .250 and you see his play at second base."

"You sure seem to know a lot about him," said Tom.

"Well, it's all there in the data," said Bob.

"Sometimes I feel I know my Airbnb host better than my congregants," said Tom.

"Well, it's all there in the data," Bob smiled.

The Pirates played well on the last Friday of August, walking out of Coors Field with a convincing 9-4 win.

"Thanks for everything tonight Bob. See you in a couple weeks at the Padres game and give my best to Dana," said Tom getting to his feet and sliding the 3x5 cards into his pocket.

"Always good to be with you Tom," said Bob. "And it's a go for a double date next month— You and Amy, Dana and me."

"Oh, great. I'll let Amy know," said Tom. "Should be a kick!"

Tom had so much to think about walking home that night. All that stuff about jobs to be done and the bell curve on innovation. I'm on a growth journey for sure, thought Tom and I guess it is Bob who is the catalyst to my growth. His thoughts were interrupted by the distinct sound of Francis' voice and guitar. He was singing Adele. Tom drew closer to hear the words.

"Sometimes it lasts in love, but sometimes it hurts instead."

Tom clapped as he walked towards Francis and put a five-dollar bill and some change into the guitar case. Francis smiled.

"So, how are things going Francis?" asked Tom.

"Not too bad. I made around $50 tonight," Francis answered.

"What's the best thing that happened to you this week?" Tom asked.

"Oh, I checked with the Shelter and they just received ten new laptops for guests to use on their premises. They said if I bought licensed copies like Illustrator, WordPress and Photoshop that I could install them, and they would reserve that computer for me to do my work any day between nine and five. I've almost saved up the money or I could do that today. I'm about forty bucks short so, that's a step in the right direction," Francis said with a faint smile.

"That's great! I'm really happy for you Francis" said Tom. Drawing on what he had learned from Bob, he asked, "What's the toughest challenge you had this week?"

"Well, I still don't have a permanent address. If I did have an address, I could start advertising and handing out business cards. Yea, I just need a permanent address that shows I'm not a flake or something. That's my biggest challenge I guess," said Francis.

"What are you going to do about it?" asked Tom.

"What kind of question is that? If I knew the answer, it really wouldn't be a problem, would it?" asked Francis.

Tom felt stupid for asking the question Bob had given him, so he pivoted. "I'm sorry Francis. Hey, I talked with my wife, and if this works for you, we'd like you to use our address as your permanent address for the next six months and then see what happens from there. When your mail comes in, I'll give you a call and you can come by and pick it up or I can bring it to you," said Tom.

"You really mean that?" asked Francis.

"Absolutely. Here's our address. It's just a couple blocks from here so it should be easy to coordinate," said Tom, handing Francis a half sheet of paper. "And here's forty bucks towards the software you need."

"I'll start building my website tomorrow," Francis said with hope in his smile.

Tom walked home thinking about a definition of friendship someone shared with him. A true friend weeps with you when you weep and they rejoice with you when you are rejoicing. Could Francis actually be his friend? he thought. Yeah, Francis is my friend.

At home
Amy greeted Tom at the door. "About time you got home. How was your night?"

"Oh, it was good. Got great stuff from Bob and I'm thinking there's something more we can do for Francis beyond letting him use our address for his mail."

"I've been thinking the same thing, Tommy," said Amy and for the next hour they began to hatch a plan.

Chapter fourteen

At church

Tom was in the home stretch of his series on Nehemiah. Today he was in the penultimate chapter and he was going to preach on the dedication and celebration of the completed wall. Singers and musicians from all over Israel had come to Jerusalem, camping in tents outside the city. Tom found this passage to be a rich opportunity to talk about the very human need for celebration, sacrifice and community. He talked about Woodstock and showed a one-minute YouTube clip of Queen's Freddy Mercury singing a call and response at the 1985 Live Aid Concert. EEEEEOOOOOO. Many in the under 60 crowd sang along. "People are born to sing and celebrate," Tom said. He talked about his non-believing cousin whose life was changed on the final night of Burning Man in the Nevada desert. "People need to celebrate as much as they need water. It's the way God made us." Tom finished by talking about the musicians being supported by the Jewish community at the same level as those who guarded the city gates. "People need beauty as much as they need bread. Societal hope and change can come from any of the domains of society...including the arts." He went on to tell the story of Josiah Wedgwood, the father of English pottery, who was part of William Wilberforce's Clapham Society, seeking to outlaw the slave trade. Wedgwood made jewelry, dinner plates, bowls, pitchers and spittoons with the picture of an African slave on his knees, hands chained but clasped and extended towards heaven with the inscription, "Am I not a man and a brother?" "God used an artist to pierce the conscious of a nation that led to the ending of the slave trade in England," Tom concluded. "In the same way, God can use you, wherever you are, whatever your craft or occupation, to change the world."

After the service Harold walked briskly towards Tom and coming so close to Tom that Tom could feel his demon breath, said. "'Hope and change!' You sounded like Obama up there. And do you know what Burning Man is? It's a pagan festival! How do you expect to bring good fruit from a bad tree? Pastor Arnie's probably spinning in his grave right now," fumed Harold.

Tom was actually smiling on the inside but kept a straight face. He knew he'd be gone in a couple weeks. "Thank you, Harold for your feedback. I'll keep it in mind for the eleven o'clock service." Tom didn't change a thing and even more people sang along with Freddy Mercury.

"I think you were wonderful this morning Tom," said Amy. "Gutsy and insightful and wonderful!" I just wish we heard more from Queen. *'All we hear is Radio Ga Ga, Radio Goo Goo, Radio Ga Ga,'* she sang with a smile.

"I'm glad I have one person who loves me," Tom said. "Let's grab some lunch and take a drive. The aspen are turning."

"And winter is coming soon," said Amy.

"Winter is coming indeed," said Tom. "Now where did I put my keys?"

At church in the all-hands meeting

Tom had been looking forward to the all-hands meeting on Monday. It was time for their second Sprint report out towards their epic wins. "Okay, Marlene I believe you have our devotion this morning."

"I sure do Tom," said Marlene with a smile. Marlene was Tom's Executive Assistant. In her early 60s, she had been assistant to Pastor Arnie for 27 years before Tom arrived. Recently divorced at the time, she desperately needed a job and answered an ad in the Denver Post for a "Girl Friday" to answer phones, stuff envelopes and run personal errands. It was a job, and she was delighted to be working. It was six months into her job when she came forward at a Sunday evening service and gave her life to Christ. Undereducated but smart, she began "growing like a weed," so they said, devouring Christian books, Christian worship and becoming a student of the Bible. And she genuinely tried to reflect Christ in all she did. A couple years later, she married Gordon, a math professor from the University of Colorado. She was a good person and Tom looked forward to what she had to say.

"So, with all our emphasis on data these past few months, I thought this week I'd get into the book of Numbers," Marlene said. "In chapter 13 Moses sends out twelve spies into the land of Canaan and asks for seven pieces of data. What's the land like? Are the people strong or weak? Are the people few or many? Is the land good or bad? Are the towns unwalled or fortified. Is the soil fertile or poor? Are there trees or no trees in the land? And then Moses asked them to bring back some fruit of the land. Because fruit takes cultivation, fruit can only be produced by a people who are settled and not nomadic. So, fruit would tell them a lot."

Tom liked where Marlene was going.

"So, when the spies returned, they all returned with the same data regarding what the land was like. They even came back with the abundant fruit of the land. But analytics is what we make of the data. So, two groups of people looked at the same evidence and came to different conclusions. Ten of the spies said, 'If we go in there, we're going to get our butts kicked.' Joshua and Caleb looked at the same data and concluded the exact opposite. 'We should go up and take possession of the land, for we can certainly do it. Don't be afraid of the people of the land, because we will devour them. Their protection is gone, but the Lord is with us.' Analytics is always a human endeavor, so our jobs are safe. The difference between Joshua and Caleb and the other spies was that Joshua and Caleb brought more data, about God and his promises, into the equation. And that led to a different conclusion. It's like John 12 where a voice came out of heaven but some people said it was just thunder. Same data, different interpretations. But we just always need to bring God into the analytics and the path forward."

"That was superb Marlene," said Tom.

Fourteen Fridays - 160

"Thank you, Pastor," Marlene said and then added "All Scripture is inspired by God…even the book of Numbers."

"Thanks again for getting all your Sprint Slides in. So, I think you remember the drill. Each team leader should introduce his or her team and then you have 5 minutes to walk us through your slide. So, we'll start with you Steph."

Experiment #2 Outcomes		Date: __/__/____
What problem were you solving for? (Attract, Get, Keep, Grow or Multiply?) What is the concise statement of the problem you were trying to solve:	Hypothesis #2: "We believed, if we did _____ _____ _____, it would lead to more of / less of _____ _____ (our desired outcome)"	Experiment #2 What you did: How you measured it: Results:
What would an "Epic Win" look like?	Notes:	What you learned: Persevere or Pivot (Circle one)

Stephanie quickly introduced her team and began. "Our team is experimenting in the Attract lane. The problem we are solving is making people in the city aware we exist and what we are known for when people think of us. Our six-month epic win would be wherever we go in the city, whoever we talk to, when we mention that we are part of Daybreak Church that people would respond, 'I've heard of you guys. I like what you're doing.' We saw in the data that the vast majority were introduced to Daybreak Church through a friend. Our hypothesis was that if we made it easy for the Daybreak crowd to tell a story of something good Daybreak Church was doing in the community, it would kill two birds with one stone. They'd know about Daybreak Church and we'd be known for doing something good. So, our experiment started back in August when we bought five-hundred backpacks and then seventy-five of us filled them with school supplies and brought them to Denver Public Schools for the teachers to give to under-resourced kids, making the teachers the heroes, not the church. Then I asked all of our volunteers, 'How many had a great morning?' and everyone cheered. Then I said, 'Tell five people on Monday, 'I had a great weekend,' and then shut up. If God is involved in the conversation, there will always be curiosity and questions. So, if that person asks, 'What did you do?' simply answer something like, 'I and seventy-five of my closest friends stuffed five hundred backpacks filled with school supplies and gave them to East High School. You should have seen the excitement on the Principal's face. And we do a lot of other things like that and are having the time of our lives.'"

"Well, what happened?" asked Tom.

"I checked in a week later and our people talked with an average of 3 people each. Just by telling our story there are another 225 folks in Denver that know about us and a bit of what we do in the city. Oh, Tracy...one of the women on my team led one of her co-workers to Christ and maybe there are others. So, we learned that people who are reluctant to say, 'Oh, my pastor's sermon was so good this week,' are more than eager to talk about the impact our church is making in the city. So, we want to persevere with our service to and with the community *and* pivot by encouraging our people to tell others of what they are doing."

The staff nodded in approval. "That's so simple a caveman could witness like that," Elliott, the High School intern said.

"Well, then you qualify," jabbed Juan good-heartedly.

"Good job Steph. You and your team are doing great with community engagement. Okay, James you're up."

James, the Communications Coordinator, introduced his team and began. "We are solving for how we might double our number of first-time visitors by doubling the number of Daybreak Church people who invite someone to our service or event...from our normal 10 percent to 20 percent of our folks inviting someone in a six-month time frame. Our six-month epic win would be that every Daybreak person would have invited someone to Daybreak Church. From the data we saw that two-thirds of Daybreak Church attendees invited at least one person to Daybreak Church in the past six months. But 30 percent of the people who attend Daybreak Church weekly invited three or more people. Only 10 percent of people who attend once or twice a month invited three or more people to church. So, the data seems to say the more frequently one attends Daybreak Church, the more likely they are to invite others. So, our hypothesis was, if we can increase the frequency of attendance, the more people would be invited to church. Our experiment was using cutting edge marketing designed by our inner-city middle school kids to get people to attend more frequently. So, you may have seen their graffiti art over urinals or inside the stalls of the men's room and lady's room:

"YOU DON'T PEE JUST ONCE A DAY, WHY ATTEND CHURCH ONCE A MONTH. SOME THINGS IMPROVE WITH FREQUENCY" I.P. Freely

"WHEN YA GOTTA GO, YA GOTTA GO. WE JUST WISH YOU'D GO (TO CHURCH) MORE FREQUENTLY" Lou Stules

"WE'D JUST LIKE TO SEE YOUR BUTT HERE EVERY WEEK" Seymore Butts

WANT TO BE PART OF A REAL SMOOTH MOVEMENT? COME TO CHURCH EVERY WEEK" B.M. Stinx

"I realized after it was too late that I was actually being punked by the junior-highers. So, the big learning was not to bypass Kaiya in any effort to work with middle school students so I'm pivoting in my Get strategy. Again, I apologize Kai."

The staff couldn't stop laughing. Tom controlled himself and said, "Remember, there's no such thing as 'failure,' just validated learning. Thanks James." Then he started laughing again. "Let's take a quick break. I've got to go to the Men's room just to read the graffiti and get control of myself."

The spirit was relaxed and light-hearted when Kaiya introduced her team and began. "When we looked at the results of the 3-Minute Survey we saw that around 90 percent of the new people chose Daybreak because of the pastor and his preaching—that was true for Pastor Tom and Pastor Arnie. But only 38 percent of our people said that the pastor and his preaching was the reason they *stay* at Daybreak, which ranks near the bottom of the reasons people stay. So, the data seems to be saying that we need good teaching to *get* people, but good teaching alone will not *keep* people. And I think that explains why so many people leave after a few months. Our epic win would be to close the back door to people leaving Daybreak Church. Our hypothesis was that if people who came to Daybreak Church because of Tom and his preaching could get some time with Tom and Amy, Tom could put them on a solid growth path that will result in more people staying and contributing to Daybreak Church." Kai looked around the room to be certain she had the staff's attention. "Our experiment was for Tom and Amy to host a catered dinner each month for all new people and explain the growth and impact journey and then invite them into the First Steps Class where they would be introduced to the things like small groups and service...the things that people do who stick around with a church. As for the results, Tom and Amy hosted two Daybreak Church dinners on the last Thursdays of the month and had a total of twenty-one people join them. Of those twenty-one people, seventeen joined the First Steps Class led by Jerome. So, we learned a ton from this experiment. We've been starting to say around here, 'Relationships catalyze growth,' so for new people the only people they feel they may know is the preacher, so an invitation by Tom is much more catalytic than the invitation from a stranger. We also had a bunch of surprise learnings."

"What were they?" Tom asked curiously.

Kaiya picked up where she left off. "Our first learning was that during the 4-week class our newbies became friends with each other and often started sitting with each other at church. So now they had friends at church which greatly increased the stickiness of the church. I was reading this week that Twitter did something similar. They discovered that if people followed just ten other people on Twitter, they started using Twitter, so Twitter gave them suggestions for the first ten people they should follow. So, our First Steps classes provide those first ten friends so to speak. The second surprise learning was the power of service. In the fourth class, there is a bit of teaching on Matthew 25 and then the church van pulls up and the class piles in and they take sandwiches to the homeless on Colfax Street. The service unites the class and fulfills their desire to serve. Sixty-eight percent of people say they stay at a church in order to contribute and so right away, the start their church involvement by 'feeding the hungry.' And, because Jerome leads the class, the participants now feel they have a relationship with a second staff person. There are so many wins on this, we are going to persevere with this idea."

"So very well done, Kai. Amy and I have really enjoyed those dinners and I hear great things about how you structure the First Steps Class Jerome. So, tell us about what you did with Grow, Jerome," said Tom advancing to the Grow slide.

"Thanks Pastor Tom. The problem we are solving for is under 'Grow.' So, we saw from the data in the Three-Minute Survey that 81 percent of respondents mentioned that they came to church to 'get closer to God.' The survey also showed that only about half regularly felt closer to God during our service. Our epic win would be for 100 percent of our people to regularly feel the presence of God in a Daybreak Church service. Our hypothesis was that if we could create an environment where people could experience God's presence or hear God's voice that more people would feel closer to God. For our experiment these past seven weeks I've stopped opening our services in prayer. I've stopped praying on behalf of people. If you've noticed I've said something like, 'Let us bow our heads in prayer. Now take a moment to ask the Lord for what you want and need out of this next hour...now pray for the person on your left that he or she might be touched by the Spirit of God this morning.... Now, pray for the person on your right that he or she would hear from God this morning. Amen.' Then if you noticed how I closed the service. I usually said something like, 'There's someone in your life that needs help with relationships this morning. Let the Lord bring someone to mind. Got that person? Now pray this verse, inserting his or her name into the prayer. Now there's going to be someone who is struggling with finances. Listen and the Lord will bring someone to mind.... Got him or her in mind? Now pray this verse...' So, for the past seven weeks we've had zero pastoral prayers, but we've created a space where people could directly hear from God and intercede."

"Oh, wow! That's brilliant," said Tanika.

"Yesterday we did a quick one-question assessment with one hundred people and 98 of them said they felt closer to God as a result of the church service. So, we pretty much doubled the sense of feeling connected to God. Bam! So, our big take-away was that people don't need us as staff to be the professional priests or intercessors. We rob them of connecting with God if we do all the talking and praying. We need to be the guide on the side more than the sage on the stage. So, we're going to persevere in this approach."

The staff looked around approvingly. "Oh…that's what you were doing Jerome," said Tom. "I didn't know what was going on and just followed along and God was regularly bringing to mind those who needed specific intercession that day. And yesterday, when you said, 'If someone came to mind who believes they are 'not enough'… that was God speaking to you, and you can help let them know they are enough,' I knew exactly who you were referring to. Thank you, Jerome. I guess I'm next."

Tom advanced the PowerPoint to the last slide in the deck. "We're in the Multiply motion. Our epic win is for 100 percent of Daybreak people to be engaged in fulfilling the mission of Daybreak Church. That they move from consumers of the mission to contributors to the mission through their giving, leading, inviting, evangelizing, discipling, etc. So, the data showed a couple of things first, of our three growth activities, giving, serving and being in a small group, giving was the biggest predictor of longevity and stickiness. In other words, giving was more likely to lead to serving and small groups that starting with small groups or serving would ever lead to giving. The data also showed that the vast, vast majority of our givers start giving within their first 180 days of regular attendance. If they don't give by then, they most likely never will. I think they look around and say, 'This church doesn't need my money, and no one's ever asked me, so I assume they're doing just fine.' Instead of not wanting to talk about money, every week we should communicate that because our mission is so big, we need all hands on deck and if you want to get involved with a venture that is changing the world that Daybreak is the place to invest your finances," said Tom enthusiastically.

"Preach it Brother Tom!" shouted Jerome. "Tell it like it is!"

Tom smiled. "So, our hypothesis was that if we are intentional about asking people to give as a first step in their discipleship path, the more likely the other good things like service, community and other areas of contribution will follow. If our heart follows our treasure, then the best thing we ask people to do is lead with their treasure."

"Come on!" urged Jerome. "Help 'em Lord!"

The staff chuckled and Tom continued. "So, our experiment was to work giving and stewardship into the third week of our First Steps class. Jerome said it was a bit awkward at first, but the response was overwhelmingly positive. One person said, 'In this church I already feel known and needed. That's never happened before.' Another said, 'I always wondered why my last church never asked us to give. I assumed they didn't need us to help them fulfill their mission. So, the overall result was, that in our first two cohorts of eight couples and six singles, twelve of them started online auto-giving and they are pretty pumped about it. The other two, who both don't have jobs, said they'd start giving regularly when they found full-time employment. So, our plan is to persevere."

The staff applauded. "Oh, one more thing. I've asked Tanika to organize another congregational survey—the same one we used last time, to see if these past three or four months have made any difference in the lives of our Daybreak people."

Friday, September 13. Colorado Rockies v. San Diego Padres

The last time the Rockies had faced the San Diego Padres in Coors Field, back in mid-June the two teams shattered the MLB total runs record held since 1929 by scoring a combined 92 runs in the four-game series. Tonight's game would be the seventeenth time this season the teams faced each other. They knew the opposing pitchers. There would be no pitch that they hadn't seen. And the pitchers knew the batters. They knew who would chase a temptingly bad pitch and who had the discipline to stand in there and wait. Tom and Bob found their seats on this warm August evening. "I bought us a couple of beers Bob and a couple bags of peanuts to keep us company while we talked. Yeah, that's the job I hired these two friends to do."

Bob smiled, "Yeah, that's a helpful concept isn't it?"

"Yeah, it's really changing my thinking on what I hire and what I fire."

Tom and Bob stood for the National Anthem and after belting out the final words "...o'er the land of the free, and the home of the brave." Tom put his Astros cap on top of his head. "I swear, someone is messing with my ball cap. This thing gets smaller every week," said Tom.

"Well, remember the climate is a lot dryer here in Colorado," said Bob.

By the end of the first inning the Rockies were leading 2-0 thanks to Nolan Arenado's home run.

"So, what's up with your T-shirt tonight Bob?" asked Tom. "Did your team run out of ideas?"

Bob looked down at his T-shirt.

"Not exactly. We bought a bunch of these T-shirts from the Waffle House to educate our team and clients on the importance of proxy data. I don't think we've talked much about proxy data since we started showing up on Friday nights. So, I wore this as a reminder. Proxy data is a great data shortcut," said Bob.

"I'm all for shortcuts," said Tom.

Bob smiled. "Well proxy data is about finding that one single data point that serves to represent a larger reality."

"I think I get where you're coming from but what would be an example?" asked Tom.

'Well, that brings me back to my T-shirt. One of the most interesting examples of proxy data is how FEMA responds to a crisis based on the Waffle House Index," said Bob.

'Wait...what?" said Tom. "The Waffle House Index?"

'It's a real thing," said Bob. "Waffle Houses never close. They are open 24-7, 365 days of the year and do their best to stay open so when they close you know conditions have to be really bad. The Waffle House operates on three levels, GREEN which indicates a full menu, full power and little or no damage at all. Then there is YELLOW, which means the restaurant will have a limited menu with no power or only power from a generator. Last is RED, meaning the restaurant is closed, which indicates severe damage, or flooding. So instead of looking at the confusing wind velocity, rate of rainfall or the temperature, FEMA takes a look at how many Waffle Houses are open and at what level."

'Who would have thought?" said Tom. "What else do you have under proxy data?"

Bob looked thoughtful. "Well, a good test of service at a restaurant is to count the number of empty water glasses. Restaurants with great service are always topping off the water glasses."

"That's a good one to know," said Tom.

Bob found the track in his brain where his information on proxy data was stored and the wheels started turning. "I have a friend who has one proxy metric before he hires anyone. He always takes the prospective employee to dinner but asks the waiter to intentionally screw up the order. Then he observes how the potential employee responds. His hypothesis is that how you treat people who serve us is the ultimate test of character and whether this is a person he wants to work with."

"Oh, yeah. I've heard a similar analogy about people who return shopping carts as the same type of test of character," said Tom.

Bob was on a roll now. "If you want to see how people feel about your city, just google "I love Denver" and "I hate Denver." If you want to know who is least likely to pay back a loan, look for keywords like, 'God,' 'promise,' 'thank you' and 'hospital' in the loan application. Or, if you want to know someone's political affiliation check out what kind of car they drive. The pickup truck replaces the elephant, and the hatchback replaces the donkey."

"These are gold," said Tom.

"There's a bunch more," said Bob. "Looking at third-grade reading levels to determine the number of prison beds a few years from now. The examples go on and on. But I do have a favorite one."

"Let's hear it Bob," said Tom with anticipation.

"Well, G.K. Chesterton said something like, 'The man who is knocking at the brothel door is unconsciously searching for God.' So, every action may actually be a data signal for something completely different. That's for us to figure out."

"So, you're saying we might want to go down to East Colfax and start a witnessing project? I mean how does all this proxy data help me as a pastor?" asked Tom.

Bob laughed. "I'm not sure but the whole idea is to start looking for correlations and see if you can turn them into facts. Like, when a person stops giving, what is that proxy for? When a person spontaneously increases their giving, is there always a bigger story behind that? Is there a single piece of data, like the Waffle House Index that tells you how you're doing as a church? I'm confident you can figure it out."

By the time the seventh inning stretch came along, the Rockies held a slight lead, 9-8. It was still anyone's ballgame and most fans were sticking around. And the pause gave Tom the opportunity to talk about something that had been bothering him. Tom told Bob about Francis and concluded, "I've been on his new website and I'd actually like to hire him for some contract work re-designing our church website and as much as I want to, I'm not sure what message that would send to the church...you know, him being gay and all."

"Well, I think it would send the message that you don't reject him whom God has accepted from Romans 14," said Bob.

"But don't you take the Bible literally, Bob?" asked Tom.

"I would say I *don't* take the Bible literally...but I do take it very seriously. Taking it literally is not taking the Bible seriously and avoids the real message. It's a shallow excuse not to think more deeply about the most important areas of life. We've substituted literal for serious."

"What do you mean by that?" Tom asked quizzically.

"Well for instance, take slavery. The Southerners took the Bible literally and continually challenged the northerners regarding their exegesis. They'd say things like, 'Slavery existed in the time of Jesus and he never spoke against it.' Or, 'If you can just show us one verse in the Bible that prohibits slavery, we will get rid of slavery.' They were interpreting the Bible literally but not seriously. Lincoln, and those in the north took God and the Bible seriously and slavery was ended. Lincoln said, 'I would never want to be a slave, therefore I would never enslave another person.' Thank God he was not a literalist," said Bob.

"Hmm...I've never thought of that," said Tom.

"I think when we focus on the faults of others, we miss out on our own need to be converted...not just getting saved but converted over and over again like St. Francis," said Bob. "We need to preach the gospel to ourselves every day."

"Wait, what? St. Francis?" asked Tom.

"Francis grew up as a rich kid enjoying all pleasures that youth could offer but renounced it all...even the clothes off his back to follow Christ. But he says his real conversion happened when he 'kissed the leper.' He said something like, 'When I became acquainted with them, what had previously nauseated me became the source of spiritual and physical consolation for me.' Sometimes to grow we need to get outside of our box. I think the job of a real man of God is to help everyone find a place at God's table. Look at the ushers here tonight. Okay, granted some of them could pass as morticians but they have one job...to help everyone find their seat. It doesn't matter if they are wearing Rockies gear, Padres gear, a T-shirt or a tuxedo, the usher helps them find a seat in the stadium. People and fans are here tonight for a bunch of different reasons, but the usher finds a place for each one. I mean, think about it, when a person goes to church on their own volition...wow...that's proxy data for so much. There better be someone who makes that person feel welcome and help them find a seat, whether they look like a true fan or not." said Bob smiling.

"Yeah, umm...I think you're right, Bob," said Tom.

Rockies' relief pitcher, Venezuelan Jairo Diaz quickly disposed of three Padres batters in the top of the ninth inning to end the game with a Rockies win, 9-8.

"I got tickets for the two seats directly behind us for the Milwaukee game. Amy and I are looking forward to being together with you two. The marriage tips you and Dana have given us were super helpful," said Tom.

"What are friends for? See you in a couple weeks," said Bob.

As Tom left the stadium, he briskly walked to the corner of Market and Park Street where he saw a familiar face. It was Francis singing, *The Dance* by Garth Brooks. The boy could sing country.

As Francis finished up, Tom came forward and put a $20 bill into the guitar case. And then Tom did something he had never done before. He extended his hand to Francis and said, "Well done Francis," and then Tom embraced him with a brief hug. It may not have been much, but he had kissed the leper. Francis teared up. "Thanks man."

From Francis' humble reaction Tom couldn't help but think that maybe he had it all wrong. Maybe it was *this* Francis who had just kissed the leper.

"I was on your website this week and was blown away by what you can do. You are a professional. And the link to other companies and church websites that you've built was really helpful," said Tom.

Now Francis was a little embarrassed. He hadn't felt that affirmed in quite some time. "It's nothing man. It's just what I do."

"So, here's what I'd like to do. Our website needs an extreme makeover and I'd like to start by having you do an audit of our website and if that goes well, I'd like you to work with our team and do a complete makeover. I don't know how long I'll be at the church, but I know we can use you for at least two weeks. So, I've got $1500 in the budget for the audit and then we'll see what happens after that," said Tom.

"You mean it, Tom?" Francis asked. "I'm all over it," he said as he danced a little jig.

"You're really good Francis. Don't forget that. I'm not just talking about your singing or your web design, you're just a good person and you are deeply loved by God himself; God has a place for you in his family and you are enough. Never forget that." Tom reached into his pocket and pulled out a 3x5 card and a pen. "Here's my email and phone," said Tom. "Let's work on this together."

At home
Tom passed through the front door and into the kitchen of the apartment. Amy patted the couch next to where she was sitting. "Come sit by me, Tommy." Tom sat down. Riley Lu joined them on the couch, lying down between them.

"You know Amy," Tom said. "I think I'm in some type of spiritual growth spurt. It's like all this crap I've been going through is actually serving as fertilizer for my growth. Do you know the story of St. Francis and the leper?"

"I don't believe I do," said Amy. "You know Tom...I think you have changed and so much for the better. Now tell me about St. Francis."

That evening Tom told Amy about St. Francis and his friend, Francis. "Look at his work Amy! This kid's a talent."

"Can't wait to meet him," said Amy. "But now it's time for bed."

Chapter fifteen

At church

Tom felt a wave of peace as he walked up on stage and took his place behind the podium. He was in the last chapter of Nehemiah and next week Pastor Ron would start a month-long series called "Starting Over." Ron was a good expositor of the Word, was well-liked and was part of the historic Daybreak family. He would do a good job and the church would be in competent hands. And he did have a track record of turning things around.

Nehemiah 13 was a difficult passage to interpret and apply literally. After being called away to Babylon for a year, Nehemiah returned to find Jerusalem in chaos and so, he began a one-man reform campaign that included beatings, violence, threats and exclusions. But although Tom couldn't apply the chapter literally, he could apply the chapter seriously. His message was about preaching the Gospel to ourselves every day and our need to be converted over and over again as we keep in step with the Spirit of God. "There is no autopilot setting for the Christian life," Tom reminded the crowd. "Like everything in God's creation, without renewal there is only decay." He ended his sermon with a moment of personal reflection and prayer by asking congregants to finish three short sentences. "As a result of what I heard this morning…
Lord, today I want to…
Lord, today I can…
Lord, today I will…
Amen"

First service pianist, Millie Hondorf did her magic on the Steinway closing the service with her rendition of "I have decided to follow Jesus" and as the older crowd exited, many were seen to be mouthing the refrain, "no turning back…no turning back."

As the second service ended Tom looked over the crowd and saw Francis smiling from the back row. A warm breeze of possibility and hope brushed past Tom's face and filled the sanctuary.

As the crowd thinned out, Amy came towards Tom and gave him a hug followed by a tight squeeze. "I'm so proud of you Tommy. You've done a great job here. And regardless of how others may see you, I'll always be your number one fan."

Amy's soothing words flowed over Tom. "Thanks Hon. Hey there's someone here I want you to meet."

At church in the all-hands meeting

Monday morning's all-hands meeting could possibly be Tom's last time together with his staff. Sure, there might be a going-away gathering but this was his last chance to influence and lead the staff. After the usual meet and greet chatter, Tom stepped up to the white board and began writing,

WHAT'S OUR DENOMINATOR?

"At Daybreak Church, we have a congregation of around a thousand active members. So, let's write down '1000' as our denominator." Tom then drew a horizontal line above 1000. "So, everything we measure, we measure as a numerator over the denominator of 1000. So, on Sunday we had 765 in attendance...so that's 765 over 1000. We have 450 in small groups...so that's 450 over 1000. We have 402 who give regularly so let's write down 402 over 1000. We have 15 full-time equivalent staff counting our interns so that's 15 over 1000. But what if we were working from the wrong denominator? Let's look at the story of the widow who put the two copper coins in the offering. When Jesus said she put in more than all the other it was because he changed the denominator to 'all that I have.' What if, as a thought experiment, we changed our denominator from 'the church' to 'the city?' What would we be measuring? Get into groups of five and let's see what we can come up with in the next 20 minutes."

What followed was a robust discussion on what a transformed city would look like. Tom ended the time with a short exercise called "Taking with and Leaving behind" where each staff took two Post-it notes and after writing their answers, walked forward and, placing their sticky note on the white board said things like, 'I'm leaving behind my narrow view of God's mission and I'm taking with me a fresh vision for the city." "I'm leaving behind a church-centric view of the Scriptures and taking away a kingdom-centric view."

Tom finished the all-hands meeting by saying, "You all know that the elders will decide if I will still be your pastor after this week. As much as I'd like that to happen, it's not in my hands and if I don't get to be with you again, I just want you to know that working with each of you...to see your progress and joy in the faith, has been the absolute highlight of my time here at Daybreak Church. We have really grown together, and we are one in love and purpose."

"Don't say that Pastor!" said Tanika. "I came here because of you. You gave me a chance and you changed my life. You can't leave. We're family." Tanika's words had given voice to what the staff felt, and they joined their voices of sadness and protest to Tanika's.

"It's not in my hands," said Tom. "And all of you have the faith, the tools and the process to take this church to the next level with or without me."

And, with a few hugs and a few more tears, the all-hands meeting was over. As he was leaving, Tom's Executive Assistant, Marlene, showed Tom a text she had just now received from her long-time friend, June. "Just want you to know, Harold and I have separated, and I asked him to move out of the house. He left this morning." Tom was stunned but rather than glee at his enemy's misfortune, he found himself feeling a wave of sadness.

That night at supper Tom and Amy talked about Harold and June. "It was something about emotional abuse that I heard," said Amy. "Serves him right. There are the laws of karma after all. I've seen him intentionally hurt you so many times Tom, I just think he finally got what was coming to him."

"Well, I thought I'd enjoy this news more…to see the demise of the man that's been trying to bring me down for the past six months, but I find myself feeling almost sorry for him. June was the love of his life. It is just….well….sad. Oh well. What do you say we start a new series on Netflix? I have the feeling I'll be having a lot of evenings free going forward."

At the elder meeting
It was the last Tuesday of September and Tom was driving to church for what would most likely be his last elder meeting. He wasn't content exactly, but he was resigned. He had fought the good fight…and lost the good fight. But as resigned as he was, Tom found himself praying, "All things are possible with Thee and if it is possible Lord, I'd really like to stay on as their pastor. But not my will but Thy will be done. Amen."

Tom walked into the boardroom to find all of the elders, minus Harold, seated around the table. They had gathered earlier in the evening to reach their final decision about Tom's future at Daybreak. The pizza boxes were still on the table. The Assistant Chairman, Russell Beeves welcomed Tom. "Have a seat Pastor." Russell went through the perfunctory opening duties of every board meeting and then opened with a short devotional from Matthew 23.

"Jerusalem, Jerusalem, how often I wanted to gather you together as a hen gathers her children, but you were unwilling."

"There are some things even Jesus himself can't do as much as he wants that thing to happen. He respects the free will of those he loves and longs to hold and be close to. Some of us wish to have relationships restored. Maybe it's an estranged friend or colleague. Some of us long with all of our hearts that we could be with our kids or grandkids, but they just don't want us in their lives. Our love and longing is there but they are unwilling. And there are people who want to be closer to us and we are the unwilling party. If any of you are in either of these situations, just raise your hand so I can see it. I'd like to pray for you." Every hand in the room went up…including Tom's. "As Pastor Tom said, 'Everyone you meet is fighting a battle. Be kind.'" And then he prayed. Tom looked around the table and saw the brokenness of every man. They…no we are all just broken human beings.

Russell turned to Tom and said, "I don't want to keep you waiting since we all know why we are here this evening and we want you to know that the elder board has come to a unanimous conclusion regarding your future here. I don't think this will come as a surprise, but this is your last week of employment at Tenth Avenue…excuse me…Daybreak Church. And we are unanimous in our decision to terminate you."

Tom's face reddened with fear and shame. The worst had happened. How could he have been so delusional in thinking this would work out? Tom looked around the room as every elder averted their eyes from looking at Tom. He was through, so with nothing left to say he walked out of the conference room and into the hallway.

There were the sounds of feet coming from around the corner. First, Tom saw Jerome then Marlene, then Tanika and Dan and Kaiya and James and Susie and Libby...It was all the staff marching toward him. "What did they tell you Tom? Are you still our pastor?"

Tom struggled to fight back the tears at such overwhelming support. "I'm afraid it didn't work out."

"We'll see about that," said Jerome. "We've got a plan. Follow me."

Jerome entered through the board room and the staff followed and they encircled the elders seated at the conference table. Tom was the last to enter, behind Kaiya.

"What's going on here?" demanded Russell.

"We just have a couple things to communicate before you adjourn for the evening," said Jerome tersely. "And we wanted to make sure you heard them before any decision you make was carved into stone."

"Well, get to it. I have blueberry pie waiting for me at home, and our decision has already been made," demanded Russell.

"I have two things to say," said Jerome. "First is about data. Tanika just now finished compiling the results of the congregation survey and every category that we measured, from small group participation, to attendance to giving, inviting, and satisfaction with their spiritual growth has gone up and to the right. Our experiments are working, and we'll continue to get better and better."

"And you'll be able to continue that upward path just fine without Pastor Tom," said Russell.

"Well, that brings me to my second point," said Jerome. "At the last staff meeting Pastor Tom said we as a staff were 'one'...that we are family. Some of us never had a real family but what I know about real family is that families stick together, and we have decided that if Tom leaves...we all leave. Our constitution says that 'we (and I quote) are elder ruled but staff led.' So, it's hard to go anywhere without leaders."

"That's outrageous! Are you threatening us?" asked Russell. "Just be patient!" Looking for help from the Executive Pastor, he spotted Dan and asked, "Do you go along with this anarchy, Dan?"

Dan nodded and smiled. "I'm afraid I do. If Tom leaves tonight all of us leave tonight. It's as simple as that."

"Just be patient and reasonable. Your actions are not only untimely but unwise. Change takes time and patience," Russell pleaded.

"That's what old white men always say to those without real power. But tonight we, the staff of Daybreak church stand united to get what this church deserves, the godly leadership of Pastor Tom. Take us all or take none of us at all." Each of the staff nodded in agreement.

Elder Russell could see that Jerome and the staff were serious. "If you could step out into the hallway, I think we can come to a decision as an elder board."

From the hallway Tom could hear the loud but muffled voices vigorously discussing his future and the future of Daybreak Church. After fifteen minutes or so, Russell opened the door and invited the staff into the board room.

"With the help of the Holy Spirit, we as the board of Daybreak Church have unanimously concluded that we want you, Pastor Tom Briggs, to be our permanent Senior Pastor at Daybreak Church and Pastor Ron will remain on as a teaching pastor. As Tanika pointed out, the numbers and giving are in an upward trend and we need to prepare for a new season of growth, thanks to you Pastor."

Tom was elated. "Thank you and praise the Lord. This is an answer to prayer and I'm very, very grateful for each one of you." Suddenly these jackass elders were transformed back into real human beings.

"Well Tom, you're free to go and enjoy the evening. We just need to finish up with the business of striping the parking lot. Again, congratulations Pastor."

Tom floated home and burst through the door. "Guess who will stay on as Senior Pastor at Daybreak Church?" he said gleefully.

"Oh, Tom I'm so happy for you. I knew it would all work out. This calls for a celebration and I bought a bottle of champagne for the occasion. Regardless of the outcome, I knew we'd be wanting a little champagne," said Amy.

Tom told the story of the amazing evening through tear-filled eyes. Amy reached for a box of Kleenex as she also was crying. "It was unlike anything I've ever experienced. It was probably the lowlight and the highlight of my life...all in one evening....I mean, next to marrying you of course....you know the highlight part." Amy understood and smiled. They had made it through together.

Tom broke the silence. "Poor Harold. Man, he's had a bad week," said Tom. "Losing this battle and losing his wife? Wow!"

"Let's not think of Harold," said Amy. "It's our celebration tonight and I've got a few surprises in store for you."

At home hosting the visitor's dinner

On Thursday, Amy and Tom hosted twelve visitors at their home for dinner. Although they usually catered from the Olive Garden, this time Amy pulled out her cookbook from Playa Borracha and created a Mexican feast. Tom was at his extroverted best and Amy made everyone feel like they'd be best friends going forward. The tide had turned.

Tom slept fitfully on Thursday night and it wasn't because he had eaten too many chile rellenos. His mind was on Harold. On Friday morning Tom gave him a call. "I'm so sorry to hear about you and June," he began. Harold had taken the week off from his teaching duties and was staying in a Hampton Inn, not far from the church. Could Tom come over and see him? "Yes, please come over," said Harold.

Tom was to meet Harold in the lobby of the Hampton Inn where they'd grab a cup of free coffee. Harold was waiting for Tom dressed in a T-shirt, shorts and a pair of gray Crocs. Tom didn't know Harold even owned a pair of shorts, but the Crocs did seem fitting. Tom began. "Again, I'm so sorry to hear about you and June and I just wanted to know what I can do...what the church can do to help."

Harold held back the tears. "Tom, first of all I have something I've been needing to say to you."

Tom braced himself for what was coming. Harold found his voice. "I want to apologize to you for being such a first-class jerk these past six months." Tom was stunned. Harold continued. "I'm really sorry and I am asking for your forgiveness." Tom nodded empathetically but said nothing. Harold continued. "Maybe knowing a bit of my story will help. I grew up in the projects here in Denver. My dad was a harsh man. He was one of the town drunks. He had a violent hot, trigger-fused temper, especially when he was drunk, and he'd beat Ron and me regularly with a leather belt or a switch. My life as a kid was a 24/7 nightmare, and our home was a living hell. My mom was sympathetic but powerless against my father. I was determined that everything that my dad was, I would be the opposite. So, he was a drunk, I'd be a teetotaler. He was hot-tempered, I'd be measured. He was evil, I'd be a saint. So, when I got saved, I got a new family here at the church. Pastor Arnie practically adopted Ron and me. Almost every moment we weren't at school, we were at his house. He discipled us. We memorized Scripture together. He believed in us. Ron and I worked as paid custodial staff at the church, so we didn't have to depend on our family to get by. Well, eighteen months ago I got word that both my dad and mother died in a one-car accident. Dad was drunk and he drove off the road and hit a tree. I don't know why, but I cried. I mourned for the family I never had, and I yearned for the church family I had growing up. And a few months later my spiritual father Pastor Arnie died. I felt so lost and alone. So, last January, when Ron talked about coming back to Colorado, I just wanted this to happen so badly…to have a real family, like it used to be. I wanted us to work together like a couple of brothers in the way we used to clean the church. I wanted it so bad that I compromised all I know to be right to get what I wanted. I did everything I could, with the backing of our feckless elders to break your spirit but you stood strong. You earned the position of Senior Pastor. June saw right through me…what I was trying to do to you…my compromises…how it was consuming my life… and now I'm paying the price. My life is nothing without her. I'm so sorry, Tom."

Tom was stunned. Why didn't he see it? If a man at the door of a brothel was searching for God, what did a man's spiteful anger mean except that at some point, he had been severely wounded. "I forgive you from the bottom of my heart, Harold. Today begins a new day of friendship."

Harold started sobbing and Tom put his arm around Harold. "Get your stuff. You're coming to stay with me and Amy. We have a spare bedroom and you're going to get your wife back."

Friday, September 27. Colorado Rockies v. Milwaukee Brewers
Tom and Amy enjoyed the walk down to Coors Field. The ambient energy of the crowd buoyed their spirits. "Oh, we need to stop by and say hi to Francis. He's doing an amazing job on our website audit and I think we may have a part-time spot for him on the tech or media team."

Soon they were standing in the back of a small crowd watching Francis perform. He was singing Lauren Daigle's crossover hit, "I Believe." When Francis got to the part, where he sang, "Taking all I have and now I'm laying it at your feet," Tom felt his eyes well up with tears. "Thank you Lord," he found himself praying.

"He's got a great voice and some chops on that guitar," said Amy.

"Yeah, I told you he was good," said Tom. He then pulled out a $10 bill and walked towards Francis and his open guitar case. There was a new block-lettered cardboard sign that read.

I AM ENOUGH
(BUT CASH IS STILL APPRECIATED)

Tom caught Francis' eye and Francis smiled as he finished Daigle's hopeful song, "Oh, what you say of me, Oh, I believe." Setting his guitar down he beckoned Tom and Amy to come closer.

"I got a call from my dad today," said Francis, filled with emotion. "He told me how sorry he was…and how much he missed me and how he wants me to come home for Thanksgiving."

Tom teared up and moved towards Francis with open arms. "I'm so happy for you, my friend. I'd like you to meet my wife, Amy."

As Tom and Amy walked away, Tom looked back and gave a thumbs up to Francis and mouthed the words, "See you Monday." Francis shook his head in disagreement and mouthed back the words, "See you Sunday." Tom smiled.

"Hey, there's something I need to do before we go inside, Amy," said Tom. Outside the stadium Tom spotted a street vendor selling Rockies baseball caps and there was a nice variety to choose from—camo, gray, purple, black and the classic black with a purple brim. Tom went for the classic. "What do you think Amy? How do I look?" asked Tom as he unlocked his phone to take a selfie.

"You look good. I like it. Somehow it really fits you." said Amy.

Tom paid the vender $15 dollars, then walked to a nearby trash can and tossed in his Astros cap.

"Why did you do that? You love that old cap!" protested Amy.

"I've outgrown it Amy," said Tom. "Like so many things, it just doesn't fit me anymore."

"Let's stop and get a couple burritos and some peanuts outside the stadium while we're at it. The food's much cheaper out here," suggested Tom.

Amy yanked at Tom's arm halting his progress. "I'm a cheap date Tom...but not that cheap. I'm not going to eat burritos out of a cooler. I go to one game a year. You can buy me a hotdog inside the stadium."

Tom relented and they went through the entrance at 20th and Blake, only pausing to take a selfie to remember the moment and worked their way up to their seats. "You're really going to like Bob and Dana. They're a great couple and are sort of our marriage mentors."

The Milwaukee Brewers were in town for the final three games of the season. It was hard to believe that all this was coming to an end. The Brewers had an outstanding season with an 89-71 Win/Loss record. The Rockies were coming into their final three games a record of 69-91. The late September weather was ten degrees warmer than usual and it was a great evening for Tom's final game with Bob. How great that Amy and Dana would be joining them.

Tom and Amy worked their way down to the second row of Section 239, right behind Bob and Dana. When Bob heard the shuffling in back of him, he stood up to greet Tom and Amy.

"Hey Bob," said Tom. "And who's this?"

Dana stood up and turned around. "Hi, I'm Dana."

"Dana…Dana. Honey I want you to meet Bob and Dana. Bob and Dana, this is my wife Amy and I'm Tom."

Hugs were exchanged all the way around. "So nice to meet the both of you," said Amy without blinking. "Tom has told me so much about the both of you."

"Well, we've been looking forward to the four of us being together for a long time now," said Bob enthusiastically. "I say we should grab some hotdogs and start this game off right. My shout."

"Sounds good on our end," said Tom. "After the National Anthem." And standing again to his feet, Tom removed his Rockies ball cap, placed it over his heart and began belting out, 'O say, can you see…'" He looked down at his hat surprised to see the purple and black rather than the orange and dark blue. But it felt good and right for some reason. Bob looked back at Tom and smiled.

Bob and Dana went for Rockies Dogs and drinks. "I didn't think Dana would be…that tall," Tom said. "And I always pictured Dana with long blonde hair for some reason."

Bob and Dana returned with the dogs and beverages between the first and second innings. The Brewers were impressive, scoring one run on two hits, and quickly disposing of the first three Rockies batters. Bob turned around in his seat. "So how did the elder meeting go, Tom?"

"Oh, way better than I expected. It's a long and beautiful story but I actually get to keep my job and they've affirmed all that we've been doing with data. It was quite the reversal of what I was expecting…as you well know," said Tom.

"So, what did elder Harold have to say about all this?" asked Bob.

"It's kind of a long story but the short of it is that Harold is living in our spare bedroom for a while," said Tom.

"Now I've heard everything," said Bob. "Take a look at my T-shirt."

"IT AIN'T OVER TILL IT'S OVER, AND IT AIN'T OVER YET." YOGI BERRA

"You don't know how appropriate that is Bob," said Tom.

By the bottom of the third inning, the Rockies had tied the game 1-1. Bob turned around in his seat, "So you must be pumped that all your prayers have been answered and you will be the permanent Senior Pastor," said Bob.

"Well, that's just the thing. At first, I was super excited because it's like I won the lottery but I'm not sure I want the job," said Tom. Amy's ears perked up. "I've grown and changed so much and my world has gotten so much bigger in these past six months I'm not sure if I want to go back to being a full-time pastor. I feel like one of those hermit crabs looking for a bigger shell though I have no idea what that new shell would look like. All I've ever known is pastoring."

Bob went into his consulting mode. "My dad used to talk about the difference between vocation and occupation. He'd say our 'vocation' was our calling, and in the Bible, we are called to three things—to belong to Jesus Christ, to be holy and to some type of redemptive ministry. 'Occupation' is how we financially support our calling. So, when Paul was in Corinth he worked as a tentmaker as his occupation but every Sabbath he went to the temple to preach the gospel, which was his calling. Then when Timothy and Silas came to Corinth he devoted himself full-time to his calling. You are who you are Tom. Your occupation is not your vocation. You'll always be a minister no matter how you choose to pay the bills."

"Yeah, I just feel like I just need to let go of the church trapeze bar and trust that there'll be someone there to catch me," said Tom. "I've always been afraid to do that before, but I think I can do it now. My world is so much bigger than ever before, but change is still scary."

"I get that, I really do. Changing careers, marrying Dana, moving to Colorado. But it's only on the other side, after letting go, that you make the growth and change real."

Going into the bottom of the sixth inning, the Brewers still held the lead, 2-1. Bob restarted the conversation with Tom. Amy leaned in towards Bob as he turned around so both could hear what he had to say. "I know this is coming out of the blue, but I want to create another alternative for you and Amy. For the past six weeks, Dana and I have been talking about how great it would be to have you on our team as a partner. We'd like to make you an offer to join us full-time and open up our church division, helping churches with data, analytics, messaging and playbooks around the Church Engagement Framework. I mean I've already trained you over the past six months and I think you'd multiply your ministry impact by helping hundreds of pastors multiply their impact. Same vocation...just a different occupation."

Tom was stunned.

"Amy, I think your husband would be amazing at this job."

"There's no doubt about that," said Amy. "You'd not have a harder and more dedicated worker."

"You don't think I know that? Everything I've even suggested to Tom he has implemented. Now imagine the impact he'd have helping hundreds of other pastors do the same?" said

Bob. "Here's an official 'offer letter' I drew up for you. It's a standing offer so you can sign it any time and all this kicks in."

Tom's eyes quickly went to the annual salary, which was half again of what he was making at the church. And that didn't count the potential bonuses which could add another fifty percent to his top line. Tom showed the letter to Amy, who smiled and nodded with approval.

Tom had never felt more valued and affirmed. He had two great offers to consider and Amy would be fully behind either choice. What a difference a day made.

In the bottom of the sixth inning the Rockies came alive. Right fielder, Charlie Blackmon, led off by hitting a four-bagger over the right center field fence. The next four of five batters made it safely on base so when Raimel Tapia knocked one over the fence into deep right field, it was a grand slam. By the time the sixth inning was over the Rockies led, 8-2.

Bob turned around towards Tom and Amy. "I say we take off and go find a little place where the four of us can grab a drink and talk more about your future before the hoards are released. I think the Rockies have this one in the bag. But before we go, I have to tell you a little story."

"We're all ears," Tom said.

"Do you ever notice how a pitcher handles the ball before he settles down to throw a pitch? Look at him. He rolls the ball around in his hand for a while and then he lets his fingers find their exact placement around the seams of the ball. I don't know if it's a coincidence or not but every baseball has 108 stitches and every Rosary contains 108 beads used for prayer and intercession. I'd like to think of that baseball as a player's set of Rosary beads, so when pitchers are rolling that ball around in their hand that each of those stitches, like the Rosary beads creates a connection between God and people, reducing the distance between heaven and earth. And I'd like to think that some of those prayers reaching into heaven, each Friday night during our time together came on your behalf Tom, to help show you the way and to help show me the way."

"Thanks Bob. Such a beautiful thought. I hope it's true...I hope it's true," said Tom.

"One more thing before we leave. Dana and I both feel a need to get reconnected to a church and were actually thinking of coming to Daybreak Church but weren't sure how we'd be received. Do you think that ushers could find a seat at the table for people like Dana and me? I mean, after all we are..."

"Friends of mine? Absolutely!" said Tom with finality. "And if I have anything to say about it, you'll have the best seat in the house right next to Amy and me," said Tom.

"I have the feeling 2020 will be a great year," said Bob.

"A great year indeed," said Tom.

But, while Tom was still speaking, an unseasonal chilling breeze, a lucky wind, whooshed through the stadium and caused many to shiver. Change was in the air.

Appendix A

Glossary of Terms

A/B Testing is comparing the results of one component, action or feature against another to see which gets better results towards the desired outcome. So, for instance, Crossroads Cincinnati Church presented two different Facebook ad sets to advertise their annual Men's Campout. One ad got four times the open rate as the other ad. Daniel introduced A/B testing when he asked the king for permission for him and his men to eat vegetables only for ten days and then compare their strength to those who ate the king's luxurious fare. A/B Testing is not limited to comparing two variables. Crossroads could have placed a dozen more ads to see which one performed best. In 2009 Google's Marissa Mayer tested 41 shades of blue to see which color users clicked on the most. Maybe she was following Solomon's advice to "sow your seed in the morning, and at evening let your hands not be idle, for you do not know which will succeed, whether this or that, or whether both will do equally well" (Ecclesiastes 11:6).

Actionable insight is the desired outcome of looking at data and analytics. The Data Literacy Project notes, "The great challenge in the Fourth Industrial Revolution is not capturing data but turning it into actionable insights."[1] People who are good at extracting value from data like to say that "'interesting' is the enemy of 'actionable.'" The idea is that data is valuable when it can inform decision making. The men of Issachar were experts in finding actionable insight. "They understood the times and so knew what Israel should do" (1 Chronicles 12:32).

Analytics is the process of applying a structured method to discover and understand relevant insights and patterns from data in order to solve a business or ministry problem. As they say, "Data is about numbers. Analytics is about decisions." There are four types of useful analytics:

1. Descriptive analytics—discovering what happened in the past to bring us to our current reality. How did people discover your church? Why did they decide to visit for the first time? Why do they stay? How do they grow? Why do they contribute? Once you discover what drives each of these behaviors, it's relatively easy to create an experiment to increase the actions that drove these behaviors.
2. Diagnostic analytics—discovering the "why" behind the behaviors. During WWII teams of very smart people were trying to figure out where to put bullet proof armor on fighter planes. From the evidence, it seemed that most of the returning planes had bullet holes in the fuselage and not in the engine. It was Abraham Wald that theorized that there were no holes in the engine because those planes were

---

[1] The Data Literacy Project Partners with QLIK to Launch World-First Comprehensive Certification for Data Literacy (https://dataanalytics.report/news/the-data-literacy-project-partners-with-qlik-to-launch-world-first-comprehensive-certification-for-data-literacy/5748). May 13, 2019

shot down so never returned. They were fatalities. So, when you want to discover why people are leaving your church, it's important to query "who did not come back."

3. Predictive analytics—based on the actions of the past that brought us to the present, what actions are we seeing in the present that most likely predict what might happen in the future.

4. Prescriptive Analytic—is about what will happen. It comes from turning "we think" into "we know" because of the repetitive patterns and consistent outcomes. e.g. "We know that if we have visitors over for dinner that 83 percent will join our new members class."

Average is simply the sum total of all the numbers divided by the number of participants. e.g. The average length of time people stay in one church is 13.5 years. However, the **mean** time (half the people stay more time and half the people stay for a shorter time) a person stays in the same church is 6.6 years.

Batching or cohorts allows churches to see what actions influence change. In December of 2017 Seacoast Church in Mount Pleasant, SC had 877 adults who identified themselves as first-time guests. This cohort served as their control group. What did they do without any intervention or follow-up? How many started giving on their own? How many joined a small group on their own? How many started serving on their own? This data served as their baseline date. Each month thereafter they introduced variables like personal invitations to a new members class, a follow-up phone call from a pastor, etc. to see which actions increased the cohort's growth and impact journey.

Bayes, Thomas was a Presbyterian minister in the 1700s who came up with the idea that predictions need to be routinely adjusted whenever a piece of new information becomes available. The research and writing of his first book, *Divine Benevolence, or an Attempt to Prove That the Principal End of the Divine Providence and Government is the Happiness of His Creatures* (1731), may have very well formed the seeds of his theories on probability. Today Bayes' theorem is used to update the probability for a hypothesis as more information or evidence becomes available. Bayesian thinking allows us to get smarter and wiser as more and better evidence becomes available.

Build-Measure-Learn cycle is a feedback loop that is one of the core components of the lean startup methodology, popularized by Eric Ries. Its goal is to turn "what if" assumptions to "what is" reality through iterative experiments that lead towards progress.

Business Question is the question that clearly defines the problem you are trying to solve. The more precisely you can define your business question, the better hypotheses you can form and the more appropriate experiments you can run. Formulating a great business question is the first step to running a data experiment.

Calendar rhythms for churches seem to follow a similar pattern, both in the liturgical calendar or the school calendar in the northern hemisphere. Advent Season (Christmas) to Lent (Easter) to Pentecost (Mother's Day / end of school year / beginning of summer vacation). Because there is such a long time between Pentecost and Advent, most churches have a "back-to-school" emphasis which gives them four big weekends to attract new visitors to their church. Thom Rainer suggests having another big weekend, such as Founder's weekend, where churches celebrate their heritage. Or it may be an annual big weekend of service projects in your community. Crossroads Cincinnati hosts their "Super Bowl of Preaching" on Super Bowl Sunday each year which has been their biggest Sunday attendance of the year. The high attendance watermarks, where the most unchurched people attend, traditionally, are Christmas Eve, Easter and Mother's Day. We suggest you plan these events within the Church Engagement Framework. You've solved for Attract and Get but what can you do at these weekends to Keep, Grow and Multiply?

Causation and **Correlation** sometimes create confusion and part of your job is to figure out the difference. Correlation is about two or more events that seem to be connected through coincidence but not causation. Correlation looks for the relationship between two or more things with the hope of being able to explain how one thing drives another. North Point Church discovered that people who were involved in two or more growth experiences had a 97 percent retention one year later. If people don't get engaged in the first 160 days a year later, they most likely never become engaged. An illustration of correlation as being totally separate from correlation is pointed out Nate Silver who points out that "From Super Bowl I in 1967 through Super Bowl XXXI in 1997, the stock market gained an average of 14 percent for the rest of the year when a team from the original NFL won the game, but fell by almost 10 percent when a team from the original AFL won instead...only a 1-in-4,700,000 possibility based on chance alone."[2] Sometimes your task is to figure out which part of the data is cause and the other part is effect. For instance, a recent national study of large churches showed "The more the global mission emphasis, the higher per capita giving." Does increased global missions drive giving or does abundant giving drive increased global missions? How would you find out? A 2012 study of used cars showed orange painted cars had roughly half the defect rates of other cars of the same make and model.[3] This type of data can show correlation but not causation.[4] Analytics can only prove a relationship (A-><-B) whereas testing can prove causation (A->B...In summary, analytics is analysis of past data to get insights and show relationships. Testing is creation of new sample data through controlled experiments to derive insights and prove a causal relationship. Analytics can prove a relationship whereas only testing can prove causation.

---

[2] P 185 signal and the noise

[3] Mayer-Schönberger, Victor and Kenneth Cukier. Big Data. First Mariner Books (New York) p. 67

[4] Jain, Piyanka and Puneet Sharma. Behind Every great Decision: How anyone can use business analytics to turn data into profitable insight. AMACOM. New York. 2014. P.30

CCPA (California Consumer Privacy Act) is a California state statute designed to insure the data privacy rights and protection for residents of California. The CCPA is the de facto standard and will most likely influence the passage of similar legislation in other states. "The intentions of the Act are to provide California residents with the right to:
1. Know what personal data is being collected about them
2. Know whether their personal data is sold or disclosed and to whom
3. Say NO to the sale of personal data
4. Access their personal data
5. Request a business to delete any personal information about a consumer collected from that consumer
6. Not be discriminated against for exercising their privacy rights."[5]

Nonprofit organizations, including churches, are exempt from CCPA regulations but leading churches are voluntarily putting themselves in compliance with the law.

Christian insanity is doing the same thing over and over again, but this time with more prayer, and expecting different results.

Church Engagement Framework serves the operating system of every church. All church programs or initiatives run on this operating system. Developed by Eric and Matt and tested by some of the largest churches in the U.S., the Church Engagement Framework explains the five things every church must solve for in order to grow and thrive.
1. *Attract*: The ability to make people aware that your church exists
2. *Get:* The ability to get people in the door for the first time—whether for a weekend service or a special event
3. *Keep:* The ability to retain visitors and start them on their engagement journey
4. *Grow:* The ability to grow disciples in your church's growth model whatever that might be
5. *Multiply:* The ability to develop leaders who are *multiplying the mission of the church* through their *leading* of small groups and ministry initiatives, *giving, serving* internally or externally, *inviting, discipling* and *advocating* for the church. We usually call these congregants "engaged" because they are engaged in *multiplying the mission* of the church

---

[5] https://en.wikipedia.org/wiki/California_Consumer_Privacy_Act

Every church, physical or online, must solve for these five motions. Churches thrive and grow based on their ability to solve for each motion by creating hypotheses and running experiences to discover what works and what does not work. Attract and Get apply to people in the city that you *don't have* in your church. Keep, Grow and Multiply pertain to the people you *do have* in your church.

Like the staves of a barrel, it is not what you do best that determines your future, but what you do worst that determines your future. Study the diagram below to more fully understand the Church Engagement Framework.

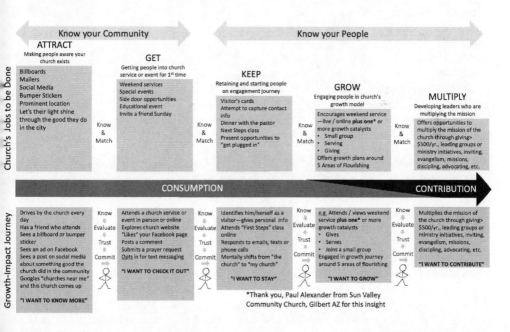

Know your Community — **Know your People**

Church's Jobs to be Done

ATTRACT — Making people aware your church exists
- Billboards
- Mailers
- Social Media
- Bumper Stickers
- Prominent location
- Let's their light shine through the good they do in the city

Know & Match

GET — Getting people into church service or event for 1st time
- Weekend services
- Special events
- Side door opportunities
- Educational event
- Invite a friend Sunday

Know & Match

KEEP — Retaining and starting people on engagement journey
- Visitor's cards
- Attempt to capture contact info
- Dinner with the pastor
- Next Steps class
- Present opportunities to "get plugged in"

Know & Match

GROW — Engaging people in church's growth model
—live / online **plus one*** or more growth catalysts
- Small group
- Serving
- Giving
Offers growth plans around 5 Areas of Flourishing

Know & Match

MULTIPLY — Developing leaders who are multiplying the mission
Offers opportunities to multiply the mission of the church through giving> $500/yr., leading groups or ministry initiatives, inviting, evangelism, missions, discipling, advocating, etc.

Know & Match

CONSUMPTION — **CONTRIBUTION**

Growth-Impact Journey

ATTRACT:
- Drives by the church every day
- Has a friend who attends
- Sees a billboard or bumper sticker
- Sees an ad on Facebook
- Sees a post on social media about something good the church did in the community
- Googles "churches near me" and this church comes up

"I WANT TO KNOW MORE"
Know → Evaluate → Trust → Commit

GET:
- Attends a church service or event in person or online
- Explores church website
- "Likes" your Facebook page
- Posts a comment
- Submits a prayer request
- Opts in for text messaging

"I WANT TO CHECK IT OUT"
Know → Evaluate → Trust → Commit

KEEP:
- Identifies him/herself as a visitor—gives personal info
- Attends "First Steps" class online
- Responds to emails, texts or phone calls
- Mentally shifts from the "church" to "my church"

"I WANT TO STAY"
Know → Evaluate → Trust → Commit

GROW:
- e.g. Attends / views weekend service **plus one*** or more growth catalysts
- Gives
- Serves
- Joins a small group
Engaged in growth journey around 5 areas of flourishing

"I WANT TO GROW"
Know → Evaluate → Trust → Commit

MULTIPLY:
- Multiplies the mission of the church through giving> $500/yr., ministry initiatives, inviting, evangelism, missions, discipling, advocating, etc.

"I WANT TO CONTRIBUTE"
Know → Evaluate → Trust → Commit

*Thank you, Paul Alexander from Sun Valley Community Church, Gilbert AZ for this insight

Working off of a common operating system allows for interoperability among every church in the world. Because every church in the world is solving for the same five problems, ideas and solutions can be curated, categorized, shared and continually adapted and improved.

The Church Engagement Framework is not only useful at the macro level for every church but is also useful for every ministry within the church, if that ministry is to grow and thrive. Every ministry lane in the church needs to solve for these five problems.

	ATTRACT	GET	KEEP	GROW	MULTIPLY
CHILDREN					
YOUTH					
MILLENNIALS					
YOUNG FAMILIES					
ADULTS					
SENIORS					
ONLINE					

Churn is the percentage of congregants that stopped attending your church during a certain time frame. You can calculate churn rate by dividing the number of regular attendees you lost during that time period, say in a 6-month period by the number of attendees you had at the beginning of that time period. Churn is often hidden if you have more people coming in the front door than you do leaving out the back door. Crossroads Church in Cincinnati discovered that people leave their church for one of three reasons: 1) the church just wasn't for them (too big, too loud, etc.), 2) They were promised friendship and community through small groups or service but never experienced it and 3) the church was not there for them during a time of crisis or loss. Could you create actions or interventions that might mitigate against the churn?

Complicated and complex problems describe two types of problems we face. Complicated problems might be very difficult, but the answers have been discovered. We solve complicated problems through discipled execution and follow-through. Complex problems (sometimes called "wicked problems") are problems for which there is no known solution so the best we can come up with is a hypothesis and experiment to validate or invalidate our proposed solution. An HBR article[6] documented the progress of 116 early-stage start-up businesses in Italy. In a blind study, half the companies were instructed in the scientific method of creating and testing hypotheses, while the other half relied on intuition and traditional business development pracices. At the end of one year, the companies using the scientific method produced an average profit of $9200 versus $1063 for those companies that did not. What can your church learn from this?

Consumers and contributors are the binary descriptions of every person in your church. Every person in your church is either a *consumer* of your spiritual goods and services or

---

[6] https://hbr.org/2020/11/founders-apply-the-scientific-method-to-your-startup

they are also a *contributor* to fulfilling the mission of your church. (Of course, contributors still consume.) We call contributors "multipliers" since they are *multiplying* the mission of the church through their giving, leading, serving, etc. Remember that people are more fulfilled through contribution than mere consumption and every consumptive activity has a law of diminishing returns attached to it.

Customer (Congregant) Lifetime Value is the total worth to a business (or church) of a customer (or congregant) over the whole period of their relationship with a business or a church. It's an important metric as it costs five times more to acquire a customer and congregant than it does to keep an existing customer or congregant. If the average congregant of Protestant churches gives $17/week and stays for 6.6 years their congregant lifetime value is $5,834. If the same congregant gives $100/week over those 6.6 years, the lifetime value would be over $31,000.

Data is the information we need to make better decisions that align with fulfilling our God-given mission. Good data encourages us to cooperate with reality rather than competing with reality. It's been said, we can have our own opinions, but we can't have our own facts.

Data Advisory Board is an advisory board made up of congregants who, because of their jobs, education, hobby or interest can help guide the church on the data, analytics and messaging journey.

Data informed is the use of intuition and data that leads to powerful insights that result in better decisions in view of fulfilling our mission. We distinguish "data-informed" from "data-driven" in that data-driven implies that we merely follow the numbers. Data informed implies a lot more inquiry and human involvement. Data without an opinion is just information. Opinions without data are just opinions. The key is to lead with data followed by an actionable opinion. Christ Fellowship Church in Palm Beach Gardens, Florida codified this phrase in their missional approach. They would be "Spirit-led, Christ-centered, data-informed."

Data informed decision-making process typically involved six key steps
1. Know your mission
2. Clarify the problem you are trying to solve on the way to your mission
3. Create a hypothesis of what you think might work in solving this problem
4. Run an experiment to test your hypothesis
5. Measure the results
6. Persevere in this direction if results are positive or pivot (a change in your tactic but not a change in your vision) if your experiment did not prove your hypothesis.

Data literacy is the ability to read, understand, and communicate information found in data sets. Data literacy also includes the ability to apply the best hypothesis and best methodology and tools for solving the business questions.

Data science is the science of turning data into value through pattern recognition, insights or predictive models. In 2012, *Harvard Business Review* described data science as the "sexiest job of the 21st century."

Data Visualization is the presentation of data in graphs, charts, symbols, maps, timelines, dashboards, scorecards, etc. that most people need to understand the meaning of data and help them move forward. Data visualization provides an accessible way to see and understand comparisons, trends over time, outliers, and patterns in data. Kevin Penry former Ops Leader at Life.church, compares visual data to a dashboard on an airplane as an illustration of the difference between flying by sight and flying by instruments. On a clear day, pilots do very well flying by sight. But when fog, darkness, clouds or inclement weather obscure our way forward we need to rely on the dashboard. Data visualization, like the dashboard, gives us the ability to see what we cannot see through observation alone. It is good data combined with good judgment that makes a great leader.

Decision science is about discovering and putting into practice the outcomes and insights that come from the data, hypotheses and experiments. The outcome you desire. You can become a decent decision scientist by focusing on just two things
1. The outcome you desire
2. The variable element(s) or behavior(s) that move the needle towards getting that outcome.

Distributed trust was introduced to us by Rachel Botsman in her book, *Who Can You Trust?: How Technology Brought Us Together and Why It Might Drive Us Apart.* For most of the history of mankind, trust was localized. A picture of localized trust is seen in the movie *It's a Wonderful Life* (1946). Deals were done with a handshake because everyone in town knew who was trustworthy and those who were not. As populations grew, we looked to trusted institutions, like church, civic and governmental leaders. Today, however our most reliable source of trust is distributed among average people like us. So, we ride in Uber because we trust the ratings of her 5,000 plus riders.

Dunning Kruger Effect—Where people mistakenly assess their cognitive abilities and practical capabilities as greater than they are. e.g. Sixty-five percent of people classify themselves as "smarter than average." This may also apply to senior pastors who assume they are smarter than the other staff or board, simply because they have the title of "senior pastor."

Elegant Solution is a solution that solves a problem in the simplest and most effective manner getting the maximum result for the minimum of effort. An elegant solution is fluoridating our water system that greatly improves dental health. Iodized salt was the elegant solutions that solved for disfiguring goiters for everyone. What are your elegant solutions? Being in a small group? Having daily devotionals? What single solutions solve multiple problems?

First, second and third-party data are the three most commonly used terms to describe the data we collect on our congregants (first-party data), another entity's first party data that they share with us (second-party data) and finally the data prediction models that emerge from big data (third-party data). First party data comes from guest cards, baptism records, assessments and congregational surveys like the Net Promoter Score. The vast majority of our business or ministry problems can be solved with first and second-party data.

From "Thus saith the Lord" to "It seemed good to the Holy Spirit and to us..." (Acts 15:28) describes the experimental approach we take to discover what works...what solves our problem. Without certainty, we define what we are solving for, create a hypothesis and run an experiment. This is what Jonathan did with his armor-bearer in 1 Samuel 14:6—"Come, let's go over to the outpost of those uncircumcised men. Perhaps the Lord will act on our behalf. Nothing can hinder the Lord from saving, whether by many or by few." Jonathan was saying, "Here's what we know about God, so let's give it a shot."

GDPR (General Data Protection Regulation) is the European Union on data protection and data privacy in the European Union (EU) and the European Economic Area (EEA). The GDPR's main purpose is to give control to individuals over their personal data and to simplify the regulatory environment for international business by creating one unifying the regulation. The GDPR has become the ad hoc worldwide standard for data privacy compliance.

Google Analytics is the most widely used website statistics service used to track and analyze your online visitors. It is used to track website activity such as number of visitors to your website, session duration, pages per session, along with the information on which site led them to your website (Google, Facebook, Instagram, YouTube, etc.). This is valuable if you are creating ads on those four platforms, because you can discover which platform produced the best results for you. You can also discover which type of ads (video, photo, words, etc.) produced the greatest results. Google Analytics also tells you age, gender and city they are in.

Google N-gram Viewer (https://books.google.com/ngrams) is a cool tool for discovering how often words or phrases have been used in over 30 million books from the 1500s to our present day. So, you can see, for instance, "Great Commission" was cited more in the 1810s and 1850s at twice the rate as it is today. Type in "fake news" and see what happens.

Google Trends (trends.google.com) is a free tool from Google that provides data and graphs on the popularity of specific search terms used on Google and YouTube from a global region, country, state, metro area or city. This feature is very helpful in understanding what people are searching for. As an insightful experiment compare three topics—relationships, marriage and porn and see what you discover.

Growth and Impact Journey is the path a congregant takes towards spiritual growth and societal impact. Their experience follows decisions and actions along the Church Engagement Framework. "I want to know more" (Attract), "I want to attend" (Get), "I want to stay" (Keep), "I want to grow" (grow) and "I want to contribute" (Multiply). Our research shows that there is almost always a trusted person in the gap between each step who encourages their growth and impact journey.

Harvard Flourishing Program

In 2016 Harvard University launched their Human Flourishing Program to discover and promote the factors that lead to human flourishing. Led by Dr. Tyler VanderWeele, they discovered that human flourishing consists of five characteristics:

- Happiness and life satisfaction
- Physical and mental health
- Meaning and purpose
- Character and virtue
- Close social relationships

VanderWeele and his colleagues discovered there the four prominent paths to flourishing are:

- Family
- Work
- Education
- Religious community

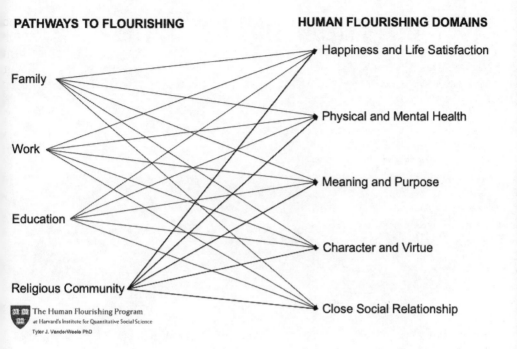

PATHWAYS TO FLOURISHING

Family

Work

Education

Religious Community

HUMAN FLOURISHING DOMAINS

Happiness and Life Satisfaction

Physical and Mental Health

Meaning and Purpose

Character and Virtue

Close Social Relationship

The Human Flourishing Program
at Harvard's Institute for Quantitative Social Science
Tyler J. VanderWeele PhD

Heuristics is a fancy word for "trial and error" approach to solving a problem and is a short-cut phrase for taking a build, measure, learn approach to solving a complex problem. Learn to say, "Here at our church, we take a heuristic approach to problem solving" and you might even get a promotion.

Hypothesis is your theory of what will bring about the desired cause and effect. It can be phrased in a number of acceptable ways, but a most common form is as follows: "If we do _____ (an action we will take), we believe we will get more (of positive) or less (of negative) of _____ (our desired outcome)."

Insight Engine is a visual tool developed by Eric and Matt to explain the ongoing process of Build-Measure-Learn. We begin with data, then we add more data (demographic, psychographic, sequence or time stamps, etc.) until we can analyze what the data is trying to tell us. This takes us to insight, which leads to developing a hypothesis and then running an experiment and measuring results—new data. We do this over and over again until we achieve our desired outcome.

The Insight Engine

Internet of Things (IoT) refers to the billions of things (and people) around the world that are now connected to the internet, all collecting and sharing data. Anything with an on and off switch can be part of IoT. This includes everything from cellphones, refrigerators, washing machines, coffee makers, lamps, heating and air-conditioning systems, thermostats, surveillance cameras, dishwashers, and almost anything else you can think of. With so much data being shared, these devices and the entire system can actually "learn" from user behavior to better serve the end user by ordering office supplies or a carton of milk or notifying you of alternative routes to work in case of an accident.

Jobs to be done is a concept developed by Clay Christensen to describe what people were "hiring" products and services to do in a different time frame. A "job" is shorthand for what an individual really seeks to accomplish in a given circumstance with a product or service. So, a father might "hire" a milkshake from McDonalds to keep him company driving to work in the morning and "hire" that same milkshake to accompany a celebration of his son's Little League victory later that same day. In the same way your congregants are hiring your church to do things you may have never thought about. You may think they have hired your church for good Bible teaching while they really may have hired your church to provide them social connections for their latest multi-level marketing business.

Know and Match is part of a bigger and more important sequence of how we add value to the lives of others. Recognized by entrepreneur, Scott Beck, Know and Match is part of the fuller sequence of *Connect-Know-Match-Catalyze* describes what people developers, including pastors, do as a way of life. The process works something like this: Between services...

- You introduce yourself to someone you don't recognize who has just poured himself a cup of coffee at your Higher Grounds Café. You extend your hand and say something like, "Hi, I'm Pastor Buck Russell" (CONNECT).
- You then ask a series of questions regarding sports, interests, marital and family status, work situation, past church involvement, where they came from, where they are living etc. You are trying to understand their needs, wants, struggles and dreams...after all they came to church for some reason. "So, Bob, you're a pretty good 3rd baseman..." (KNOW).
- "Well, we've got a great mens softball team. Took third place in the city rec league last year. There's our coach now...Dr. Titus Finkter. He's our local proctologist and a heck of a coach. 'Doc, take off your glove and shake hands with Bob here. Bob was an all-league third baseman at Boulder High and I told him we have quite the team.'" (MATCH). "Matching" is about connecting people to appropriate next steps in their spiritual journey. Its about sending the right message to the right person at the right time through the right channel.
- Bob joins the softball team and the accompanying men's small group and the cycle is complete (CATALYZE).

We continually connect, know, match and catalyze with both the people in the community or people in the church.

Know and trust is the process visitors and congregants go through before they take their next steps in their growth and impact journey. It is shorthand for "Know-Evaluate-Trust-Commit." Knowing and trusting someone (even at a distance) allows people to answer the questions, "Will I attend?" "Will I stay?" Will I grow?" and "Will I contribute?"

Key Performance Indicators (KPIs) are the elements of your plan that express what you want to achieve by when. They are the quantifiable, outcome-based, time-bound statements you'll use to measure the progress to meet your goals or objectives. Having a good set of KPIs assume you know what factors drive your church...weekend service, attendance, volunteers, small groups, giving? How do you know? What experiment might you run to find out? How would you rank the things that drive your church? For instance Brian Tome, lead pastor at Crossroads Church in Cincinnati says, "Finances are the only reliable thing to measure....The only number we know for sure that is reliable is what is happening with our giving. That's the number that can expand your influence or shrink your influence. The gold standard for giving in the current age is automatic, recurring, digital giving.... All of your other numbers don't increase your ministry."[7] People that understand data and KPIs insist that you discover and grow your most important metric.

Lean Startup is a methodology popularized by Eric Ries in his books, *The Lean Startup* and *The Startup Way* designed to shorten the product development cycles and rapidly discover if a proposed business model is viable. This is accomplished by adopting hypothesis-driven experiments (Build-Measure-Learn), iterative product releases, customer feedback and validated learning. Ries says a startup is not just a smaller version

---

[7] https://app.virtualsummits.com/membership/1479/presentation/8877/7278

of a larger company. He says a "startup is a human institution designed to deliver a new product or service under conditions of extreme uncertainty." The purpose of a startup is not necessarily to make money or to acquire customers but to discover the sustainable business model by homing in on the "product-market fit." The lean startup approach is particularly helpful for church planters or any new ministry initiative you're trying to launch. It's good to remember that "there is no knowledge in the room...just hypotheses that need to be tested in the streets."

Metrics may have been covered in our explanation of KPIs. Tiffany Deluccia of the Unstuck Group says that "everything you measure should help you make better decisions and refine your strategies for reaching people and helping them take next steps in their faith journey." We also encourage you to understand the difference between "lead measures" (the actions we take) and "lag measures" (the results we get) from *The Four Disciplines of Execution*. Is there one metric that matters more than others in view of accomplishing your God-given mission? A good metric changes the way we behave and helps us pick a course of action. A good metric should have a pullable lever attached to it—an action we can take to influence the outcome. You may want to look at what other single metrics others have discovered that have the biggest impact on the results they are seeking.

- For Moneyball's Billy Beane it was on-base percentage
- US Navy Admiral, William H. McRaven says "If you want to change the world, start by making your bed every day"[8]
- Weightwatchers has discovered two habits of people who lose weight and keep it off. They track their food daily and they come to meetings weekly
- Sociologist Robert Putnam in his book, *Better Together* tells us, "The more neighbors who know one another by name, the fewer crimes a neighborhood as a whole will suffer"[9]
- Flossing your teeth every day adds 6.6 years to your expected lifespan[10]
- Adolescents who ate family meals five to seven times a week were twice as likely to get A's in school as those who ate dinner with their families fewer than two times a week[11]
- The Success sequence: "First get at least a high school diploma, then get a job, then get married, and only then have children." Only 3 percent of people who

[8] https://www.youtube.com/watch?v=esoQKkFQoIQ
[9] Robert D. Putnam and Lewis M. Feldstein, Better Together—Restoring the American Community (New York: Simon and Schuster, 2003), p 269
[10] Jacob Franek. Six Healthy Habits for Living Longer.
(https://www.askmen.com/sports/health_400/449b_6-healthy-habits-for-living-longer.html)
[11] Anne Fishel. "The most important thing you can do with your kids. Eath dinner with them." https://www.washingtonpost.com/posteverything/wp/2015/01/12/the-most-important-thing-you-can-do-with-your-kids-eat-dinner-with-them/) January 12, 2015

follow this sequence are poor compared to 47 percent who do not follow the sequence end up in poverty[12]

- Reading by the end of 3rd grade is most likely the most determinative data point about a child's future. Not doing so is tied to graduation rates, unemployment, incarceration, substance abuse and teen pregnancy.[13]

Minimum Viable Product (MVP) is a concept from Eric Ries' that stresses the impact of continual learning in the process of product development. Eric Ries defines an MVP as that version of a new product which allows a startup team to collect the maximum amount of validated learning about customers with the least possible expense or effort. So, for instance in 1999, Nick Swinmurn hypothesized that people would buy shoes online, so, instead of investing in inventory he went to a neighborhood shoe store and asked if he could take pictures of the shoes, reassuring the owner that if he sold any shoes online that he would pay the shoe store the full retail price. That was his MVP which proved his concept and gave him the green light to move forward. When starting a new campus, program or initiative, its best to start with small batch experiments that validate your idea rather than betting the farm. Jim Collins would say, "Fire bullets, then cannonballs." Maybe God was teaching Gideon about an MVP when he asked Gideon to reduce his army from 32,000 to a mere 300.

Net Promoter Score (NPS) has been shown to be the number one predictor of the future of an enterprise. The Net Promoter Question is, "On a scale of "0" (not likely at all) to "10" (extremely likely), how likely are you to recommend our product or service to your friends or colleagues?" The score is derived from subtracting the percentage of net detractors (0-6) from the percentage of the net promoters (8-10). Any score over zero is considered "good." Any score over 50 is considered "great." And any score over 70 is seen as "world class." The NPS is a great first experiment to run as it has a 90 percent correlation to congregant engagement. By adding additional questions as Daybreak's Pastor did you may get insights on which activities lead to higher engagement.

Occam's razor is attributed to the English Franciscan Friar and theologian, William of Ockham (1287-1347) who developed this theory while defending divine miracles of the Bible. William proposed that the simplest theory, consistent with the data is most likely to be the right one. So, most likely Jesus' actual bodily resurrection is the most plausible explanation. Another corollary of the razor is that when presented with competing hypotheses about the same prediction, one should select the solution with the fewest assumptions.

---

[12] George Will, Listen up millennials. There's a secret to success. https://www.washingtonpost.com/opinions/listen-up-millenials-theres-sequence-to-success/2017/07/05/5a4a8350-6011-11e7-a4f7-af34fc1d9d39_story.html. July 5, 2017
[13] Early Warning: Why reading by the end of 3rd grade matters: A Kids Count Special Report by the Annie E. Casey Foundation. https://www.ccf.ny.gov/files/9013/8262/2751/AECFReporReadingGrade3.pdf

Personas are research-based characters, which you create in order to represent the different user types that you may want to attract to your church or the people currently within your church you're trying to grow. Creating personas will help you to understand your users' demographics, needs, behaviors, skills, goals or fears and the place your church has in meeting those needs. You are not your user. Developing personas can help you achieve the goal of creating a good user experience for your target-user group by bringing the right message to the right person at the right time, through the right channel.

Platform is a business model designed to connect contributors to consumers in real time. Platforms are based around four concepts:
- Latent energy— Platforms help that which "wants to happen," turning passive longing into active energy
- Core interaction—The singular action, that if multiplied and scaled, fulfills the mission of the platform organization. "Know and Match" is the basis for most core interactions
- Scale—The rapidity to reproduce the core interaction along with the speed and ease of which consumers can become contributors. In platforms producers and consumers are not people but *roles*. And it is very easy to shift between the roles of consuming and producing
- Tools— Designed to *remove all friction from the core interaction* so that the core interaction is increasingly simple, repeatable and common. Ideally platforms don't do any "work" per se but *create tools* for people to do the great work themselves.

Population is a collection of people or things you want to understand. It could be congregants or people in your community.

Proxy data is a singular piece of data that represents a larger reality. For instance, a study from Wayne State University analyzed the smiles of 230 Major League Baseball players from the 1952 player baseball cards to determine how positive emotions influence longevity. Players with no smiles lived an average 72.9 years; those with partial smiles lived an average of 75 years; and those with big, authentic grins lived an average of 79.9 years, the researchers found. Facial expressions can be proxy data for longevity. In our church world the data shows when a person stops giving, 95 percent are in personal crisis or are about to leave the church. When a person's regular giving goes up or down it always signifies that the giver is experiencing a major life event and a great time for a personal visit.

Regression Analytics is the most common statistical technique for predicting the value of a dependent variable (such as sales) found in the Y axis in relation to one or more independent variables (such as number of salespeople, the temperature or the day of the month) found in the "X" axis. We call this methodology "Start with Y" as the "Y" axis defines what we are trying to accomplish while the "X" axis forms our variables of how we might accomplish "Y."

Sprint "is one timeboxed iteration of a continuous development cycle. Within a Sprint (usually one to six weeks), a planned amount of work has to be completed by the team and made ready for review."[14] Teams share what they did along with the outcomes, learnings and their next iteration in the Build-Measure-Learn cycle. Sprints are all about "What we can do in this time block (Sprint cycle) to make progress toward our "epic win." All Sprint work is in service to accomplishing this epic win. Sprint methodology is designed to make us smarter and wiser with each Sprint cycle. Through "validated learning" we see what's working and not working towards our epic win. The feedback from the results is what we get (the "Learn" from the Build-Measure Learn Cycle).[15] We then "pivot" or persevere based on what we learn.

Uberization of ministry is the term coined by Matt and refers to the shift in opportunities available to pastors and leaders today to think more like Uber than Yellow Cab. Now that ministry tools can be curated, and trust is distributed to individuals there has never been a more opportune time to equip and release the saints for the work of service. This is what has always wanted to happen!

User journey (See Growth and Impact Journey)

Validated learning is one of the most important concepts to come out of the lean startup movement. Validated learning comes as the last step of the Build-Measure-Learn cycle and is the result of what you learned from your hypothesis and experiment results. As you are inching your way towards effectiveness there is no such thing as failure…just validated learning.

Vanity metrics are metrics that may be flattering but are not actionable. Such vanity metrics might include "Likes" on your Facebook or Instagram page. Vanity metrics might include "emails sent" while "emails opened" tells the real story. Viewers of your sermon may be a vanity metric while those who shared your sermon are a better measure of effectiveness.

"Very Disappointed" Survey measures if what you are offering your congregants or community is scratching where they are itching. Just ask those folks who are using the product or service, "How would you feel if you could no longer use the product or service (Think the 8am service, small groups, free childcare at date night, men's retreat, food pantry, etc?" and then measure the percent who answer, "very disappointed." After surveying and benchmarking nearly a hundred startups, startup guru Sean Ellis found that 40 percent was the magic number to indicate the viability and growth trajectory of a product or service. So, a company like Slack has 51 percent of users who would be "very disappointed" if they could no longer use Slack. Here is the complete survey that will help you move forward.
    1. How would you feel if you could no longer use _____?

---

[14] https://yodiz.com/help/what-is-sprint/
[15] https://steveblank.com/2015/05/06/build-measure-learn-throw-things-against-the-wall-and-see-if-they-work/

a) Very disappointed
b) Somewhat disappointed
c) Not disappointed
2. What type of people do you think would most benefit from _____?
3. What is the main benefit you receive from _____?
4. How can we improve _____ for you?

Appendix B

Seven Helpful Analytic Tools

There is nothing like a great tool when you're looking to get a job done. The right sized hammer, a set of screwdrivers, a miter box, a set of wrenches, a variable speed drill helps us build or repair most anything we want. What are your top go-to tools? Tools give greater ability to the willing. Tools magnify human desire into results and help us do something we want to get done. The better we are at using the tools, the quicker the job gets done. In the world of data and analytics there are seven helpful tools that anyone can employ that can lead to actionable insight. Let's take a look.

1. Aggregate analysis is the most commonly used analytics methodology.[16] It is also the first step to using other methodologies. Simply, it is a description of a population that you want to understand—your congregation or a subset of your congregation. This information comes from your first party data—the data you collect on your own congregants so it would include age, gender, attendance, small group involvement, giving history etc. Aggregate analysis shows what your congregation looks like. You can use aggregate analysis to discover:

- Who are our congregants?
- How do my congregants differ from one campus to another or from one service time to another or one age group to another?
- Who joined the church over the past three years? And then do an aggregate analysis on where these people came from. Are they new to town or discontent church people looking for another church?

Aggregate analysis can provide insight to target people who are similar to the demographic we already have. Since we attract who we are (even more than who we want to attract) aggregate analysis is the basis of creating "Lookalike" ad campaigns through Facebook.

2. Correlation analysis "looks for the relationship between two or more things with the prospect of being able to explain or drive one with the other."[17] So when LCBC Church in Manheim, Pennsylvania discovered that if a new attendee had ten intentional engagements with the church in the first 16 weeks, they had a 280% higher chance of being engaged at LCBC than those who had fewer than ten intentional engagements they were using correlation analysis. This insight led them to create a 16-week on-boarding process for newbies. North Point Church in Alpharetta, Georgia discovered that people who were involved in two or more growth experiences (giving, serving, small group) had a 97 percent retention rate while those involved in only one growth experience had a retention rate of under 60 percent. Sun Valley Church discovered the stickiness of a

---

[16] Jain, Piyanka and Puneet Sharma. Behind Every Good Decision: How Anyone Can Use Business Analytics to Turn Data into Profitable Insight. AMACON Publishing, New York, (2015) P.37
[17] Ibid. p. 38

second growth activity apart from church attendance. They called their initiative "Plus One." Correlation analysis serves as the basis for A/B testing with ad sets or church offerings. Crossroads Cincinnati Church used correlation analysis when trying to discover how length of a sermon series affected drop-off rate.

3. *Trends analysis* "is aggregate or correlation analysis over time."[18] Are we growing, shrinking or maintaining over time? Are there any internal or external events that interrupted or impacted the trend lines (economic downturn, firing of a popular pastor, unexpected massive global pandemic, etc.) Trends analysis seeks to answer "Why?" When North Point Ministries looked at the trends of child enrollment, they noticed that parents enrolled their kids in the highest numbers right after they were born. Enrollment decreased till around age 11 when it spiked nearly as high as when parents enrolled their newborns. After age 11 child enrollment declined steadily to almost zero by age 18. Seeing the trend allowed the leaders at North Point to understand that parents wanted to get their kids involved in church right before their teen years which gave them the insight to start a "finding a faith of your own" initiative with pre-teens.

4. *Sizing and estimation* "is a structured approach to making a near accurate guesstimate in the absence of historical data. It is typically used to make a business case for going into a new market, to understand the potential marketable universe for a product yet to be launched, and to quickly size up the impact of a decision or change."[19]

---

[18] Ibid. p. 40
[19] Ibid. p. 40

Radically New Audience		45-min Thursday Evening Service
Adjacent Congregants		
Existing Congregants		
Existing Services and Programs	Adjacent Services and Programs	Radically New Services and Programs

So, sizing and estimation might be helpful in creating hypotheses on how you might reach more people, not by doubling down on something you already are doing but by offering something *radically new* to people you typically are currently not reaching. Based on a hunch, one of our friends in Colorado started a 45-minute Thursday evening service, complete with children's program (*radically new offer*) to reach busy, outdoor-minded Coloradans (*radically new market*) who like John Muir find themselves thinking, "I'd rather be in the mountains, thinking about God than in church thinking about the mountains."

5. Predictive analytics "looks at current and historical data to make predictions about future events."[20] Brought to public attention through the highly publicized example of Target knowing a teenage girl was pregnant before the girl's father knew, predictive analytics is where data takes on a magical predictive feature. The logic behind predictive analytics is pretty simple: People who are doing behavior "A" today were doing "B, F and G" behaviors yesterday. So, if we can identify people who today are doing "B, F and G" behaviors today, we can predict with a high degree of certainty that they will be doing behavior "A" in the near future. Predictive analytics has been around for a long time from FICO scores to weather prediction modeling to calculating the odds for the Kentucky derby. Predictive analytics becomes actionable when we can intervene once predictive data becomes available. So, for instance, when a consistent giver stops giving, there is a

---

[20] Ibid. p.41

very high probability that three months later that person will no longer be involved in the church and it's a good time to arrange for a visit.

6. *Segmentation* "is an analytics methodology that groups customers or products into meaningful segments, usually to enable better targeting for the purpose of driving higher value through customization. Those in the same group are more similar to each other and different from those in another group."[21] Segmentation is the key to customization. If we want to send "the right message to the right person at the right time through the right channel" then we need to segment our audience to the granularity of our messaging. Segmentation includes such things as:

- Gender
- Relationship status
- Generation
- Income
- Spiritual propensity
- Motivations
- Etc.

Segmentation is needed anytime we want to customize offerings or incentives to specific groups of people. Think of the characters in *The Wizard of Oz*. Dorothy wanted to get to Oz because she wanted to get back home to Kansas. The Cowardly Lion wanted to go to Oz because he wanted courage to act. The Tinman wanted to go to Oz to get a brain and the Scarecrow wanted to go to Oz to get a heart. They all wanted to go to Oz, but their motivations were very different. Segmentation is sometimes also called "batching" and is used for cohort studies. As previously mentioned under "Batching," Seacoast Church in Mount Pleasant, South Carolina has broken down their new visitors into cohorts—i.e. "Class of January, 2019," "Class of February, 2019," etc. Batching allows them to test which variables cause greater stickiness or engagement over time.

Customer Life Cycle Analysis "looks at the different stages of the purchase process to determine what stage a group of customers is in to decide how to move them up to the next stage."[22] What we, as a church, need to master is built around our church's operating system--the five things churches need to do to thrive and grow:

- Attract people
- Get people
- Keep people
- Grow disciples
- Multiply leaders

Do you know how people hear about your church? Do you know why they decide to attend for the first time? Do you know why they decide to stick around and maybe how they decide to get involved in a growth journey. Why do they decide to multiply the mission of the church through their giving, leading, serving and advocacy? Do you know what

---

[21] Ibid. p.42
[22] Ibid. p.43

happens in the gaps between each of these stages? Understanding the Church Engagement Framework will help you understand your congregant's journey along with the enablers, blockers and barriers. What if you learned that in nearly every gap there was a person who invited them into the next step? What difference would that make?

7. *Regression Analytics*[23] is a fancy phrase used to define something we call "Start with Y." And we think of this process as the most powerful of the seven tools. It serves as a perpetual experimentation engine that helps you find your optimum solutions to problems you're trying to solve or goals you are trying to achieve. Let's look a little closer.

Start with your "Why" and your "Y"

Your vertical "Y" axis serves as your goal—something important to you or important to the future of your church. Your "Y" declares to the world what you're solving for. Without your "Y" there is no "why." To quants, this vertical Y axis is known as the "dependent variable" and for you and your church it is your goal you're trying to achieve or problem you're trying to solve. Most likely it is built around Attract, Get, Keep, Grow & Multiply. Here might be an example:

- Increasing first-time guests
- Getting people to return a third time
- Re-activating lapsed members
- Closing the back door
- Increasing attendance for sermon series
- Increase small group enrollment
- Doubling the number of millennials
- Increase regular givers by 30 percent
- Increasing your Net Promoter Score by 10 points
- Raising $4m towards a capital campaign
- Recruiting more volunteers
- Increasing small group leaders
- Increasing digital engagement
- Etc.

X factors

Once you clarify you're your "why" ("Y")—the goal or the problem you are solving for, you can begin creating your hypotheses based on the independent variables found on the X axis. Each experiment begins with a question:

- Will increased touch points of second-time guests increase their stickiness?
- Will a person's second activity (church plus intentional giving, intentional serving, small group, etc.) lead to increased engagement?

---

[23] Regression analysis is a powerful statistical method that allows you to examine the relationship between two or more variables of interest. While there are many types of regression analysis, at their core they all examine the influence of one or more independent variables on a dependent variable.

- Will segmented Facebook messaging lead to more first-time guests?
- Does a "catchy" sermon title lead to increased attendance for that series?
- Because church people donate 40 percent of their giving in December, will we get more of that 40% if we do a December sermon series on generosity?
- If 80% of people who give to church have no credit card debt, will we see an uptick in generosity if we help people get out of debt?
- Are people more likely to recommend our church after we serve others in our community?

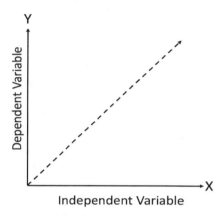

Independent Variable

Your horizontal X axis...your "independent variable" represents the actions you can take based on your hypothesis that would have an impact on your dependent variable (your "Y.") e.g. If we did more of _____(X) we believe it would lead to more of this: _____(Y). What do you do more of on the X axis that starts increasing the upticks on the Y axis? You know you have a real winner when actions along the X axis represent commensurate results on the Y axis.

Your turn to start with Y
1. What's an outcome you'd like to obtain (goal to accomplish / problem to solve)— Your "Y"
2. Create a hypothesis of what factor(s) (your "X") might affect that outcome (Y)?
3. Run a small batch experiments to validate your hypothesis
4. Measure
5. Learn
6. Rinse and repeat

Next Steps
1. We've found the book, *Behind Every Good Decision: How Anyone Can Use Business Analytics to Turn Data into Profitable Insight* to be particularly helpful in understanding analytic at a basic level. In the introduction they write that "simple analytics can actually help you solve 80 percent of your business problems at a fraction of the cost of complex analytics.... In fact, 80 percent of these problems can be addressed day to day by managers and decision-makers who have had the right exposure to simple tools and methods."
2. When you are facing a problem, start by asking, "What's the right tool for the problem we are trying to solve?"
3. Have fun...keep experimenting...keep learning! As Steve Jobs liked to say, "Stay hungry. Stay foolish."

Appendix C

Designing and Running a Data Experiment

This is the fun part. Master this simple process and you will have the tools to never be stuck again. You will have the superpower of digging yourself out of any hole you find yourself in and advancing the mission God has called you to.

Step 1: Determine what you are solving for. Typically, all of the problems you are solving for will be around the Church Engagement Framework (Attract-Get-Keep-Grow-Multiply). To these we might add "church culture" and "technology" There are three ways to begin a data experiment.

1. Start with the "business question" which succinctly states the exact, precise, specific problem you're solving for
   - If we intentionally pursued millennials, would we get more millennials in our church?
   - If we had a 45-minute Thursday night service, would we get a larger percentage of unchurched people attending?
   - Will adding a Saturday Night service significantly increase our weekend worship?
   - Does creating a 45-minute coffee time between services create more social connection and congregant satisfaction?
   - Will we increase the number of regular givers if we consistently offer one-time giving experiences?
   - Which singular growth activity (giving, serving or small group involvement) is more likely to trigger other growth activities?
   - What do people who consistently walk with the Lord and make an impact do that the half-hearted don't do?
   - Does planned, online giving increase the amount of the average gift?
   - Does one-time gift trigger more regular giving?
   - If someone texts "Guest" to a number, that triggers the church to donate $10 to charitywater.org (or similar organization), does that action lead to becoming a regular giver?
   - Over half of people who receive an email about a crowdfunding campaign made a donation. Can we use crowdfunding to fund youth-based mission trips?
2. Explore the data
   - What data tells you that you have a problem or opportunity?
   - Why is this a problem worth solving?
   - What would happen if you solved this?
   - Here's an example from one church (located in the south) that conducts an annual congregational survey as to why people attended their church for the first time:

YEAR	SOMEONE INVITED ME	I SAW SOMETHING ON SOCIAL MEDIA	I ATTENDED AN EVENT	I SAW A YARD SIGN-BILLBOARD	I STARTED WATCHING ONLINE	I GOT SOMETHING IN THE MAIL	I FOUND WEBSITE	OTHER
2017	1061	61	64	100	0	13	133	867
2018	1799	64	199	121	24	19	135	775
2019	2185	303	264	187	93	67	393	0

Descriptive analytics tells us what happened. What's this data trying to tell us? What story is it telling? What's trending up or down?

3. Create a hunch. Hunches are the starting line to discovery and a great method for testing and proving what you feel God may be whispering to you. A hunch is found in the phrase, "I wonder what would happen if...

   a. We cancelled Sunday morning services on the last Sunday of the summer months did a community-wide serve day in its place? Would this lead to greater engagement?

   b. We used a Kickstarter approach to funding new ministry initiatives? Would this expand our missional footprint in the city?

   c. We started a 45-minute service on Thursday evenings that included kids programming. Would we reach people that no one is currently reaching in our community?

   d. We curated the best messages from well-known pastors from around the country and included one of these pre-recorded in each of our sermon series. Would that increase congregants' willingness to invite a friend to our weekend service?

Step 2: Create a hypothesis on what factors might improve the chances of reaching your desired outcome. If it's a good one, you'll learn as much by disproving it as you would by proving it. "We believe that if we do _____, it would lead to more of / less of _____ (our desired outcome)."

Step 3: Run an experiment to test your hypothesis. From the outset, be clear on what you need to measure to produce a decisive result—and whether that's a metric you have the capability to track.

Step 4: Measure the results and record your learnings (validated learning)

Step 5: Persevere if the results of the experiment are favorable or pivot by trying another hypothesis and experiment that takes you toward your desired outcome. Remember pivots are a change in tactic, not a change in the vision or desired outcome. Rinse and repeat...BUILD- MEASURE-LEARN!

Pitfalls to consider:

- Not knowing what "success"/ "winning" looks like in Attract-Get-Keep-Grow-Multiply—Not clearly defining the problem you're solving for
- Not defining the measure of success for your project
- Not knowing your Key Performance Indicators (KPIs)—the metrics that matter
- Not tying your experiments to your KPIs
- Not knowing the drivers that lead to success / winning
- Not having a clear and transparent decision-making process
- Not having a validated learning posture
- Not having good enough first party data
- Thinking that data is a substitute for the Holy Spirit
- Failing to identify key stakeholders
- Not aligning with stakeholders
- Not having a plan for analysis
- Using the incorrect methodology when other methodologies would serve you better
- Not customizing your analytics presentation for the particular audience you are trying to persuade

Now is the time to start and you will learn as you go. Forbes' Joseph Noonan reminds us: "Don't be paralyzed and wait until you have figured out all of data analytics. Instead, move forward with quick-win projects that serve as building blocks and pave the way for deeper analytics success."[24] The above process is a great path forward.

That's all folks. If you have finished this book, you now know more than 99 percent of all other pastors and most business leaders. Don't just join the journey. Help lead the journey.

[24] **Joseph Noonan, A Crawl, Walk, Run Approach To Increasing Your Analytics IQ** (https://www.forbes.com/sites/forbestechcouncil/2019/09/09/a-crawl-walk-run-approach-to-increasing-your-analytics-iq/#1d28c2a6209c) **September 9, 2019**

Bibliography

Botsman, Rachel. *Who Can You Trust?: How Technology Brought Us Together and Why It Might Drive Us Apart.* Public Affairs Press. New York. 2017

Christensen, Clayton M., Karen Dillon, Taddy Hall and David S. Duncan. *Competing Against Luck: The Story of Innovation and Customer Choice.* Harper Business. New York. 2016

Davenport, Thomas and Jeanne Harris. *Competing on Analytics: The New Science of Winning.* Harvard Business School Press. Boston. 2007

Duarte, Nancy. *Data Story: Explain Data and Inspire Action Through Story.* Ideapress Publishing. Washington D.C. 2019

Jain, Piyanka and Puneet Sharma. *Behind Every Great Decision: How Anyone Can Use Business Analytics to Turn Data into Profitable Insight.* AMAMCON, New York, 2015

Knaflic, Cole Nussbaumer. *Storytelling with Data: a Data Visualization Guide for Business Professionals.* Wiley Publishing. Hoboken, NJ. 2015

Lyseggen, Jorn. *Outside Insight: Navigating a World Drowning in Data.* Ideapress Publishing. Washington D.C. 2017

Lewis, Michael. *Moneyball: The Art of Winning an Unfair Game.* W. W. Norton & Company. New York. 2003

Ries, Eric. *The Lean Startup: How Today's Entrepreneurs Use Continuous Innovation to Create Radically Successful Businesses.* Currency Press. Redfern, New South Wales. 2011

Ries, Eric. *The Startup Way: How Modern Companies Use Entrepreneurial Management to Transform Culture and Drive Long-Term Growth.* Currency Press. Redfern, New South Wales. 2017

McChesney, Chris, Sean Covey and Jim Huling. *The Four Disciplines of Execution.* New York. Free Press. 2016

Siegel, Eric. *Predictive Analytics: The Power to Predict Who will Click, Buy, Lie, or Die.* John Wiley & Sons. Hoboken, NJ, 2016

Silver, Nate. *The Signal and the Noise: Why So Many Predictions Fail—But Some Don't.* Penguin Books. New York. 2015

Stephens-Davidowitz, Seth. *Everybody Lies: Big Data, New Data, and What the Internet Can Tell Us About Who We Really Are.* Dey Street Books. New York. 2017

Notes, Hypotheses & Experiments

Notes, Hypotheses & Experiments

Notes, Hypotheses & Experiments

Made in the USA
Columbia, SC
07 May 2021